MW00834023

Stories about the
American Revolution

George Washington and his troops

COMMONWEALTH STORIES

FOR YOUNG READERS

Stories about the American Revolution

The Storm Breaks

The Siege of Boston

Misadventure in Canada

STORIES BY
James M. Bayne

NARRATIVE BY JAMES C. THOMPSON

COMMONWEALTH BOOKS

Alexandria, Virginia

Copyright © 2011
James M. Bayne (author)
James C. Thompson, II (contributing editor)

All rights reserved. No part of this book may be used or reproduced in any manner whatsoever without written permission except in the case of brief quotations in critical articles or reviews.

Commonwealth Books
1800 Edgehill Drive
Alexandria, VA 22307
703-407-3719
www.commonwealthbooks.org
e-mail: info@commonwealthbooks.org

Library of Congress Control Number: 2011923424 (paperback edition)

ISBN (print): 978-0-9825922-4-3
ISBN (ebook): 978-0-9825922-5-0

Cover and text design and composition by John Reinhardt Book Design
Cover Illustration: George Washington and his Troops
By Frank Schoonover (1926)

This picture is the property of the Westervelt Collection and displayed in The Westervelt-Warner Museum of American Art in Tuscaloosa, AL. It is used here with the owner's permission.

View online at: http://www.warnermuseum.org/colonialfederal.html

Printed in the United States of America

Acknowledgments

Where does one begin in recognizing the many that have been instrumental in giving you a love of family; of country; and opening the doors to opportunity?

My parents believed in this country and gave to it far more than they received. They held that we were blessed because our ancestors gave so much in order that we might be the best that we could be. My father was a Master Mason who believed and abided by the teachings he found there which included honesty, compassion, love, trust and knowledge. My Mother extended a helping hand to those in need and taught me to love the land as she had been taught.

My wife, Melba, who was just sweet sixteen when she captured my heart and who some four years later, joined me on our life's journey. She stood by me and supported my every whimsy. I know she would by happy to see this dream come true.

Mrs. Beatrice Ward was one of my early teachers and introduced me to how this country came about. Ms. Charlotte Spurlin was my American History teacher in high school and brought to life the stories of our founding fathers (and mothers). My how she loved this country,

It has been my good fortune to become friends with John Sinks, PhD who knows more than I can ever hope to learn about the founding of this nation. John has mentored me in my travels through the myriad roads of learning about people and events of the American Revolution. John has researched his family diligently and has, as of this writing, documented the participation in the AR of over 50 of his ancestors. Larry McClanahan, a former president of the Sons of the American Revolution, and a descendent of Captain William McClanahan of the original Culpeper Minute Men Battalion, has shown me that time will not diminish the memory of forebears but you need to work at it.

I would be remiss if I did not recognize the outstanding contributions to this book which my colleague, Jim Thompson, has made. Without his efforts this book would not exist. Jim has woven the web which ties together the little vignettes which I have written. His knowledge of the founding of this nation is immense and he shares with me the desire that our history not be forgotten.

Contents

Contents

Foreword

WHEN SPEAKING WITH JIM BAYNE, one quickly learns that he is a man of honor and distinction. Foremost among his distinguishing qualities, I find, are his love of country and his corresponding care for its well-being and the well-being of its citizens. It has been a pleasure and a valuable educational experience working with Jim on this project. Our plan is produce a series of "Stories for Young Readers" that retells the story of America's War for Independence. We are doing this in illustrated narratives that remember the people and events in its major campaigns.

The series begins here with stories about the siege of Boston and the ill-fated invasion of Canada. It will continue with books about 2) the war in New York, 3) how the British captured Philadelphia and the remarkable American victory at Saratoga, (4) aid from France, the grim winter at Valley Forge and the end of the war in the northeast, 5) the war in the Carolinas, and 6) the campaign in Virginia which culminated with the siege of Yorktown and the surrender of Lord Cornwallis.

Jim created the stories that appear in this book (and future books in the series) for his local newspaper. When asked how he came to this work, he explained that he volunteered to write a column remembering America's patriotic heritage after reading a celebratory article on Cinco de Mayo. Shouldn't Americans learn about America, he asked. I think so. Sallust, the Roman historian, helps us to understand why in these words:

> *"Often have I heard that Quintus Maximus, Publius Scipio and other renowned men of our commonwealth used to say that, whenever they beheld the images of their ancestors, they felt their minds greatly excited to virtue. It could not be the wax or the marble which possessed this power; but the recollection of their great actions kindled a generous flame in their breasts not to be quelled till they also by valor had acquired fame and glory."*

We are telling the tales of America's patriots in their marches, their endurance of hardships and their courage in combat, not to inspire young readers to seek fame and glory, but rather in the hope that they will learn from the examples of America's founders. Some may answer the call to undertake great things as Quintus Maximus and Publius Scipio did 2000 years ago. It is perhaps more important however to be a good citizen. What it means to be a good citizen is shown by the unselfish sacrifices our forbears made on behalf of the great virtuous cause, which was to create this country. In creating a nation founded on principles of political freedom, America's patriots secured an unsurpassable benefit for their countrymen and peoples everywhere.

One of our advisors made this comment: "I found it confusing exactly what was fact & what was fiction in the documents." Since this may be a general question, I will answer it here by observing that the history Jim relates in his stories is factual. Some details may be fictionalized to allow the narrative to flow from one story to the next. That is to say, the events mentioned in this (and subsequent) texts happened on the dates mentioned and were, with some editorial exceptions, conducted by the persons named. The narrator is a reconstruction of Jim Bayne's patriotic ancestor. We have fictionalized this brave American by placing him on General Washington's staff and giving him access to the records needed to assemble these stories. If Captain William Mackay misremembers some names and dates, that is his prerogative as a story teller. We encourage readers to verify the accounts Captain Mackay has and will include in the books of this series.

In preparing this text we consulted children's librarians, curriculum specialists and museum program planners. They have confirmed to us that the vocabulary and content of this book are suitable for middle school age audiences. We think its illustrations and maps will bring to life the people and events remembered for readers of all ages.

James Thompson
Commonwealth Books
Alexandria, VA
March, 2011

Chronology of Events: The War in the North

Book 1

THE SIEGE OF BOSTON

19 April 1775: The Battles of Lexington and Concord

10 May 1775: Fort Ticonderoga is taken

17 June 1775: Bunker Hill - General Gage's final failure

03 July 1775: General Washington takes Command of the Army

December 1775: January 1776: Colonel Knox brings the guns from Ticonderoga

05 March 1776: General Washington mans the Dorchester Heights

17 March 1776: General Howe evacuates Boston

THE MISADVENTURE IN CANADA

August 1775: General Montgomery departs Fort Ticonderoga for Canada

11 September 1775: Colonel Arnolds departs Cambridge with 1100 men

Oct – Nov 1775: Colonel Arnold sails Up the Kennebec River

05 November 1775: Colonel Arnold's depleted army reaches Quebec

13 November 1775: General Montgomery captures Montreal

18 November 1775: Colonel Arnold joins his army to General Montgomery's

31 December 1775: General Montgomery launches the attack on Quebec

April 1776: Colonel Arnold begins his retreat from Quebec

Book 2

THE NEW YORK CAMPAIGN

March–June 1776: The British Army regroups in Halifax, Nova Scotia

June 1776: General Howe and his army sail to New York

05 July 1776: General Washington orders the Declaration of Independence read to the army

27 August 1776: General Washington's Continentals are driven from Long Island

15 September 1776: General Howe's army enters New York City

16 September 1776: General Washington is defeated again at Harlem Heights

28 October 1776: General Washington suffers another defeat at White Plains

16 November 1776: A Continental garrison surrenders at Ft Washington

20 November 1776: Another Continental garrison surrenders at Ft Lee

Retreat: General Washington leads his army across the Jerseys to safety in Pennsylvania

TWO IMPORTANT VICTORIES IN NEW JERSEY

26 December 1776: General Washington wins a surprise victory at Trenton

3 January 1777: General Washington wins another daring victory at Princeton

Jan–Jun 1777: General Washington establishes his army at Morristown

Book 3

GENERAL HOWE CAPTURES PHILADELPHIA

August 1777: Where has General Howe gone?

26 August 1777: Dispatch from Metuchen

11 September 1777: A British victory at Brandywine Creek

21 September 1777: The Americans suffer a disaster at Paoli

26 September 1777: General Howe's army occupies Philadelphia

04 October 1777: Near Disaster at Germantown: General Lee fails to lead

22 October 1777: A diversion at Ft Mercer

05 December 1777: Stalemate at Whitemarsh

October 1777 - May 1778: The British change commanders

Fall 1777: The Conway Cabal

24 May 1778: General Howe sails home

A GREAT VICTORY AT SARATOGA

05 July 1777: The Americans gain a tactical victory at Hubbardton

06 July 1777: General St Clair abandons Ft Ticonderoga

16 August 1777: General Stark wins a valuable victory at Bennington

October 1777: Benedict Arnold sparks a great victory at Saratoga

Book 4

THE FRUITS OF VICTORY

06 February 1778: France Comes to America's Aid

A GRIM WINTER AT VALLEY FORGE

Dec 1777–May 1778: Dispatch from Valley Forge

20 May 1778: Giving Howe the slip at Barren Hill

THE BRITISH ABANDON PHILADELPHIA

18 June1778: General Clinton returns to New York

THE WAR ENDS IN THE NORTHEAST

28 June 1778: General Washington's army holds its ground at Monmouth

Captain William Mackay [1]

CHAPTER ONE

My Name is William Mackay

Dear William and Mary,

Here is the first of the stories I promised you. I am gathering them together so you can know how our country won its political Independence and how we achieved our proper place as a free and sovereign people. This is the greatest gift a parent can give his children. You must be careful to protect it so you can give it to yours.

Your loving Grandfather,

William Mackay

Remembering the American Revolution

You and I are now Americans.

Unlike you, I was born a subject of an English king. My father fought against the tyranny of England at the Battle of Culloden in 1745. The defeat the Scots suffered there made it necessary for him to leave his homeland forever. He chose to come to America and to start a new life here. He brought his family to Virginia, but moved soon after that to Mecklenburg, North Carolina, which is where I was born in 1751.

My father carved a farm out of what was then wilderness. I farmed with my father—like everyone else in my family. We all worked very hard to make a living and to better ourselves. My father thought it was important to have a good education. This is what he wanted most to give his children and the children of his neighbors. He therefore built a school where we all learned to read and write. It was my father, however, who taught me the most important things I know. I learned from him that all men are created equal and have God-given rights that no man can take away, that these rights include freedom to worship as the spirit calls each of us to do and to live under laws that we the people create to promote our common good.

I became a patriot when the English Parliament began to violate our inherent rights by taxing us without first seeking our consent. In May of 1775, the citizens of Mecklenburg County drafted a declaration protesting this tyranny. My father and I were among the first to sign it.

I was twenty-three years of age at that time, which was old enough to be elected Captain of the one of the first militia companies North Carolina created to defend our rights. Six months after my company mustered in, we were sent to Virginia to help our patriotic neighbors defend themselves against the aggression of their governor, John Murray, Lord Dunmore.

After news of the battles at Lexington and Concord reached Virginia, relations deteriorated quickly between the people of Virginia and Governor Dunmore. In June, he abandoned his palace in Williamsburg and moved to a naval vessel in the York River. He soon made the HMS Fowey the

John Murray, 4th Lord Dunmore [2]

flagship for a loyalist fleet that he gathered in the harbor at Norfolk. From his headquarters there, he proclaimed that he was going to "reduce this colony to a proper sense of their duty." Few thought he would.

I STARTED MY JOURNAL shortly before my company departed for Virginia. Here is my first entry. It is dated December 2, 1775:

It appears that if we are to be freemen we must soon be at war with the King. Tomorrow we march to Hampton, Virginia.

Recruiting for the Continental Army [3]

My cousin Reuben Moss, who is a member of the Culpeper Minute Men Battalion, is already in the field near there. I received this letter from him two days ago:

In the spring of this year, our Culpeper District raised a battalion with ten companies of minute men and one company of riflemen. The Colonel is Lawrence Taliafero and the Lt. Colonel is Edward Stevens. Captain John Jameson and Captain William McClanahan are two of the company commanders.

We are all eager to rid the colony of the British, but many of us have only our hunting rifles for weapons. Our uniforms consist of hunting shirts made of linen dyed the color of green leaves and across our shirt fronts are the words "Liberty or Death".

The Culpeper Minute Men Emblem [4]

We spent most of September learning to stand in formation and to march. In early October we marched to Williamsburg. We arrived on the outskirts of the town on October 20. Initially we were met with trepidation on the part of the local citizenry as they thought we looked more like savages than an army. But after learning that the tomahawks and knives we carried were for use against the British and not them we were welcomed. The pub keepers were especially happy to have us in their midst.

Our respite in the area did not last long as we received word that Lord Dunmore had ordered his troops and the British naval forces under the command of a Captain Squire to begin raids on the towns along the James River. On October 24, the Committee of Safety placed the 2nd Virginia Regiment of Colonel William Woodford on alert and attached five of our Culpeper Minute Men companies to his command.

One of Captain Squire's ships was driven aground near Hampton during a storm and a part of its crew was captured by the local militia. They removed such goods and arms as

Colonel William Woodford [5]

they could, set fire to the ship and later released the captured
seamen. The night of the 25th, Captain Squire landed some
men in the Hampton area and set to looting homes there. On
the evening of the 26th, word of these provocations reached
us in Williamsburg. The Committee of Safety there immediately ordered Colonel Woodford's regiment together with
our Culpeper Minute Men riflemen to Hampton. We were
commanded by Captain Abraham Buford.

We traveled all night in a driving rain and arrived at
Hampton about 8 o'clock the next morning. Colonel Woodford left us in a church to dry ourselves while he rode to
the riverfront to see what awaited us there. He found a
line of British ships before the town. When they began to

cannonade it, Colonel Woodford ordered us to take up positions in the homes and buildings along the river's edge. Under this cover, we held the advantage even though we had no cannons. Thus concealed and protected, we were able to pick off the British sailors as they stood at their guns.

Finding himself in an untenable position, Captain Squire ordered his fleet to withdraw. In the course of doing so, one of his ships drifted close enough to shore that we were able to capture it. After this success, Captain Buford led our company back to Williamsburg. Captain Green's company of riflemen succeeded in repelling the final attempts by the British to land again on Virginia soil.

Soon after this, Reuben's company was sent to Great Bridge where we had an unexpected reunion. I wrote this in my journal the night before we met:

The royal governor of Virginia, Lord Dunmore, declared martial law on November 15. He then freed all the indentured servants and Negroes who were willing to bear arms for the Crown. These freedmen, together with the other loyalists, brought Lord Dunmore's force to about 300 men under arms.

He has now secured the port of Norfolk—a city which has strong loyalist sentiments—and sent a detachment 20 miles west to a village called Great Bridge. By doing this, he has confirmed his intention to control the western entrance to the city. Our mission is to prevent this.

View at the Great Bridge battle site [6]

We joined the Virginians at Great Bridge on the evening of December 8 and fought the Battle of Great Bridge the following morning. Colonel Woodford was again in command. Here is a segment of the report he submitted to the Committee of Safety after the battle:

We reached Great Bridge on December 2. The village is located on a causeway that leads from the southwest into Norfolk. The country through which this causeway passes is largely swamp. Notable exceptions to this are the two small tracts that anchor the bridge at the town's edge. These plots approximate islands in a sea of bog.

The enemy had erected a crude enclosure on the solid ground at the end of the bridge nearest to Norfolk. They called it, fittingly, Fort Murray in honor of the governor. (My men called it the "Hog Pen.") A spy informed us that they had placed a cannon within it so as to command the bridge and the thoroughfare that approaches it from the west. This thoroughfare runs the length of the southern island and another 400 yards to a small church where the road divides.

8

We established our position near this point and so were within range of Fort Murray's gun. We put up a breastwork in the form of a letter "M" which provided for a defensive cross-fire in the event the enemy chose to attack us. I did not believe that an attack on Governor Dunmore's forces would succeed as we had no cannon to support our musket and rifle men.

Over the next several days we exchanged fire with the enemy. Because this firing was continuous, we began to run low on ammunition. I discovered upon inspecting the companies of militia that came in during these days that many of the men were shoeless and lacked blankets. The damp ground and chilly air aggravated their uncomfortable condition. Therefore on December 7, I sent a letter to the Committee of Safety in which I requested these items along with ammunition and other provisions.

At dawn on December 8, I sent the Culpeper Minute Men to probe the British position, but they were easily repulsed. We learned that evening that additional forces had come out from Norfolk and that these additions had increased the enemy's strength to 700 men.

As dawn broke on December 9, the enemy began to reset the planks it had earlier removed from the bridge. As he did this, he burned the buildings near his position so as to clear a field of fire. As he labored at these tasks, he maintained a continuous fire upon our pickets for the purpose of keeping us back. When he had completed these tasks, I heard the order shouted out, "Boys, stand to your arms."

A large detachment from the fort then began to advance against us. It came toward us in parade formation six abreast—no doubt because of the narrowness of the causeway and bridge. In this tight formation, our assailants could not *make a broad frontal assault upon us. After an initial volley, I ordered the troops to hold fire until they were within 50 yards of our breastworks. My riflemen then cut down the officer who led the attack and many of those in the ranks nearest to him. Without a leader, the attack stalled and its survivors began to retreat. We allowed them to drag their dead and wounded with them as they withdrew.*

My officers wanted to pursue them, but I considered the risk too great for the good we might accomplish. Orders notwithstanding, Lt. Colonel Stevens and his Culpeper Minute Men rushed forward and occupied the trench that surrounded the abandoned cannon. Once they were in position there, we were able to drive the enemy away with ease.

Colonel Woodford, being aware that I kept a journal, asked me to draft his report. When the committee finished reviewing it, it ordered me to deliver it to General Washington who was then in Boston.

Our victory at Great Bridge ended English rule in Virginia. Not long after this defeat, Lord Dunmore abandoned the colony. Soon after that, he sailed home to England. Many of Virginia's Tory sympathizers became patriots at this time. Our victory at Great Bridge also proved that America's citizen soldiers could stand against England's professional army.

CHAPTER TWO

I Became a Member of General Washington's Staff

I will begin by saying a few words about General Washington.

Five months before the Battle of Great Bridge, the Congress in Philadelphia appointed George Washington as Commander-in-Chief of its newly created Continental Army. General Washington, who was a Virginian, was our most experienced native-born military officer having served with distinction with the British army during the war with the French and Indians. Although he was not eager to be the high commander of the new "American army," he accepted the post out of his sense of honor and duty and moral obligation to his countrymen who had asked him to lead them in throwing off the oppression of England's King.

It cannot be doubted that these virtuous traits were strengthened through his adult life by his faithful adherence to the tenets of Masonry which instruct that we have a responsibility not only to develop ourselves but also to benefit others. George Washington became a member of the Masonic Lodge in Fredericksburg, Virginia in 1753. Several other leaders of the Patriot cause were also Masons. Among these were,

Washington takes command of the Continental Army in Cambridge [7]

to name but a few of those who you will read about in these stories, Benjamin Franklin, Paul Revere, William Dawes, John Hancock, and Dr. Joseph Warren. General Washington's association with men committed to the beneficent principles of the Masons surely strengthened his resolve during the trying times through which he endured.

In keeping with the principles of Masonry, General Washington stood at his post for eight long years. During this time he accepted not a penny of compensation.

After his appointment, General Washington went immediately to Boston where sixteen thousand New England militiamen were waiting should General Thomas Gage bring his army again out of the city.

The messenger came [8]

GENERAL GAGE started the war two months before General Washington took command of the army. He did this by sending a column of redcoats to Concord to confiscate the military supplies Massachusetts's patriots were gathering there. The road to Concord led through Lexington. On Lexington Green, these redcoats met a company of local militia. It has never been

General Washington studies Captain Mackay's report [9]

determined who fired the first shot, but eight of our men were killed in the exchange. The first grenadiers were killed two hours later at Concord Bridge. During the British retreat from Concord, the English learned that the war they had started would be a long and bloody one.

General Washington's first task as Commander-in-Chief was to forge the numerous colonial militias into an American army. After this, he needed to create a network of information gatherers so he could know the movements and resources of his enemy.

It was for this reason. I believe, that he took so much interest in the report I presented him. I know he liked it because

Washington confers with his generals [10]

General Washington bids farewell to his officers [11]

when he finished reading it, he offered me a position on his staff.

My job was to collect and compile the many dispatches and field reports which came to General Washington into "intelligence." General Washington then shared this intelligence with his commanders and together they created the army's battle plans.

I joined General Washington's staff eight months after the siege of Boston began. I remained with him through General Cornwallis's surrender at Yorktown in October 1781. We bid a final tearful farewell at Fraunces Tavern in the city of New York on December 4, 1783.

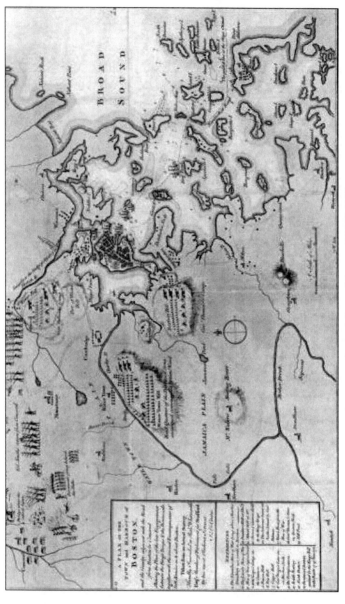

Lexington Concord Siege of Boston (1775) [12]

CHAPTER THREE

The Siege of Boston: Part 1

Lexington and Concord

These stories remember the first campaign of the war. During this campaign General Washington drove the British out of Boston. It proceeded through four phases which I recount in the next four chapters.

BOSTON WAS THE PLACE where the trouble started. It started there long before the shots were fired on Lexington Green and at Concord Bridge.

You can see from the map I have included (opposite page) that the city of Boston is like an island at the head of a bay full of islands. Its port is its life line. When Lord North closed it to punish the perpetrators of the Boston Tea

The Boston Massacre—March 5, 1770 [13]

The Boston Tea Party—December 19, 1773 [14]

General Thomas Gage [15]

Party, the city faced starvation—and the independence movement faced collapse.

General Gage arrived in Boston soon after the port was closed. (which was done on June 1, 1774). General Gage had lived in the colonies for nearly two decades by then. Nineteen years before, he served with George Washington, Horatio Gates, Charles Lee and Daniel Morgan (all of whom you will meet later) in General Braddock's disastrous expedition to Fort Duquesne. In 1767, he became the commander for all British forces in Northern America. He came to Boston in the summer of 1774 to replace Thomas Hutchinson as the Royal Governor of Massachusetts.

As soon as he had settled himself in the city, he declared martial law and began to increase the size of the British forces there. He claimed he needed the additional troops to keep the peace, but Boston's Patriots suspected that he had other intentions.

By the winter of 1774 several leaders in the patriotic party had removed themselves from the city. Foremost among these were Samuel Adams and John Hancock. Several of their lieutenants remained in the city, however, to monitor the activities of General Gage and his army. Among these were Benjamin Church and Joseph Warren who were prominent physicians, Paul Revere, a silversmith, and William Dawes, a carpenter. (Notice that Patriotism was not a matter of social rank.)

Sam Adams

Sam Adams is important to remember because he was the man who created the patriotic movement. His Christian name was Samuel, but everybody called him Sam. I found this account of him in an article among General Washington's papers:

Sam Adams was born in 1722 and was the son of Samuel Adams, Sr. The father was a prosperous businessman who was also active in local politics. His son graduated from Harvard College when he was 18 years of age. With financial support from his father, Sam entered the business world. Unfortunately, he was not good at managing money and soon failed as a businessman. Next he obtained a post from the royal governor as a tax collector, but he was just as bad managing the taxes he collected as he had been managing his business accounts.

Sam Adams pointing to the Charter of Massachusetts[16]

He married Elizabeth Checkley in 1749. She died in 1757. He married again in 1764. It was at this time that he became engaged in politics. Parliament passed the Sugar Act that year. Sam claimed that it violated the colonists' rights because it imposed taxes upon them without their approval. His argument against it soon became a patriotic rallying cry: No taxation without representation!

From 1764 through 1774 Sam Adams sharpened public opinion against the royal government by publishing a newspaper that reported how it was abusing the rights of Boston's citizens. He eventually made his readers angry enough to resist the authority of England's colonial government. His friend Richard Henry Lee carried his ideas to Virginia where they found favor with Patrick Henry and Thomas Jefferson.

Charles Thomson and Thomas Mifflin started the movement in Pennsylvania.

Late in 1772, Sam Adams uncovered a plan to change the way that the judges of the Superior Court of Judicature were paid. Until then, they had been paid through the colony's General Court. Now they were to be paid from the Royal Treasury with funds collected by the Commissioners of the Board of Customs. Sam said this would be tyrannous because it would prejudice the judgments of the courts in favor of the King and his ministers.

To protect against this tyranny, he proposed that the city of Boston create a Committee of Correspondence composed of twenty one of its leading citizens. Under his watchful eye, this committee published a series of papers that set forth the rights of the colonists and explained how the policies of Parliament infringed upon them. These papers, which came to be known as the "Boston Pamphlet," were sent to towns and villages throughout the colony. Soon every hamlet in Massachusetts had its own Committee of Correspondence and the people who lived in them looked to these committees to lead them in resisting British tyranny.

Thomas Hutchinson, who was still the royal governor at this time, called Sam Adams "the greatest incendiary in the empire" and believed that he was behind the spread of these committees. He was right to think that Sam was forming a network to promote rebellion against the King. One of his last acts, as governor was to offer Sam Adams a bribe to stop inciting the people against the King and his royal government.

When General Gage became governor, he sent an emissary to warn Sam Adams that unless he quit making trouble he would be charged with treason and sent to England for trial.

Sam answered him saying, "Go tell Governor Gage, that my peace has long since been made with the King of kings, and that it is the advice of Samuel Adams to him that he no longer insult the feelings of an already exasperated people."

This insult so offended General Gage that he issued a proclamation which stated, "I do hereby, in his majesty's name, offer and promise his most gracious pardon to all persons, who shall forthwith lay down their arms, and return to the duties of peaceable subjects: excepting only from the benefits of such pardon, Samuel Adams, and John Hancock, whose offenses are of too flagitious a nature to admit of any other consideration but that of condign punishment."

By then the war had started. Soon after that General Gage was recalled to England.

Sounding the Alarm

By mid-April 1775 it was apparent that General Gage was organizing his forces to take the field. Paul Revere, who was still operating a shop in Boston, noticed that the British were bringing their landing craft ashore for repairs. On April 16, he rode to Lexington to advise John Hancock of the impending danger. Hancock sent word to Concord, which was then a center for Patriot activity outside Boston, that the townspeople should disperse and hide the supplies they were collecting there.

This is what Paul Revere said about his trip back from Lexington:

Paul Revere observing British troops moving on the Charles River [17]

I paused on my homeward trip to meet with the Patriots of Charlestown. During this meeting we developed a plan to warn Concord in the event the British left the city. Since they could get to Concord either by crossing the Boston Neck and marching through Roxbury or by crossing the Charles River and marching through Charlestown, I proposed that lanterns be hung in the belfry of Old North Church to signal which route the British were taking. A simple signal—one lamp if by land; two lamps if by sea.

My fellow patriot, William Dawes, and I agreed to sound the alarm. I would row across the Charles River to Charlestown then ride over the Charlestown Neck through Menotomy and Lexington to Concord. Will Dawes would ride over the Boston Neck, then south through Brookline, then north across Cambridge Bridge through Menotomy and Lexington and finally to Concord.

The light in the North Church tower [18]

Our plans set, we now waited for signs that the British were preparing to move. Early on the evening of April 18, Dr. Warren received word from a trustworthy spy that the British would cross the Charles River before dawn the next morning. That night two lights shone high in the steeple of Old North Church.

Concord would be warned, but Dr. Warren decided that Sam Adams and John Hancock must also be advised of the danger as both men were wanted by the British and might be arrested. You can see from the map I have included (page 28) that Lexington was in everyone's path.

Thanks to Paul Revere, John Hancock narrowly escaped. Afterwards, he gave this account to the Committee of Safety:

Paul Revere and William Dawes left the city in the early hours of the night on April 18. Revere, bedeviled by misfortune, forgot the rags he needed to muffle the sound of his oars as he rowed past the Somerset, Lively and Falcon which were all anchored in his path across the Charles River. He reached Charlestown but barely escaped capture there and had to alter his route

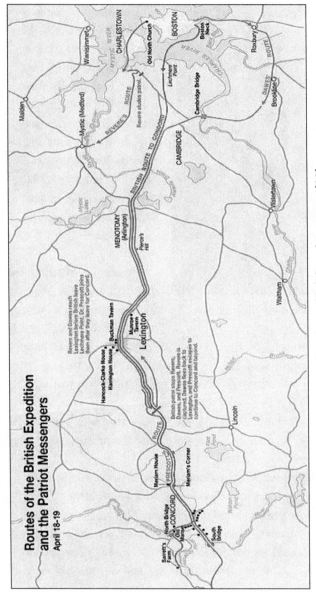

Routes of the British Expedition
and the Patriot Messengers
April 18-19

Everyone's path to Concord led through Lexington [19]

Paul Revere's midnight ride [20]

northward through Medford. In spite of these difficulties, he
reached Lexington about midnight and reported his disturbing
news that the British were coming! We were soon joined by
Dawes who repeated Revere's warning.

Having advised us of our danger, at about 12:30 a.m. on
the morning of the 19th, Revere and Dawes set off to warn
the people of Concord. Dr. Samuel Prescott joined them on
this leg of their journey. Hardly had they gotten underway
than they encountered a British patrol. Dawes was thrown
from his horse but managed to escape. Poor Revere was not so

lucky—the British seized him. Thankfully, Dr. Prescott eluded capture and reached Concord. Another group of horsemen received his message there and scattered to spread the word to our Minute Men in the surrounding countryside.

Revere's captors threatened to shoot him unless he divulged our plans. He obliged them by giving them greatly exaggerated accounts of our numbers and our knowledge of the movements of their troops. On the journey back to Lexington, hearing gunfire in the distance, his captors released him (along with other prisoners they had taken earlier in the evening) and sped off to warn the column approaching from Boston.

Because they confiscated his horse, Revere had to walk back to Lexington. When he reached the town, he found me still there. Warning me that we had not a minute to lose, we borrowed two horses and rode off. We had gone but a short way when I discovered that I had left a satchel of valuable papers at the house of Reverend Jonas Clarke (where Sam Adams and I had our lodgings). After persuading me to conceal myself, my brave companion returned to the house. He found the satchel just as the British were entering the town. He reached me again while the Redcoats were firing upon our compatriots on the green.

The Battles of Lexington and Concord

The night before his army marched, General Gage issued these orders to Lt. Colonel Francis Smith:

"You will march with the utmost expedition and secrecy. You will seize and destroy all the artillery, ammunition, provisions, tents, small arms, and all military stores whatever. . . . But you

Lt. Colonel Francis Smith [21]

*will take care that the soldiers do not plunder the inhabitants
or hurt private property."*

Lt. Colonel Smith was 63 years old. I expect that is why his
army didn't march until 9:00 on April 19.

Our most intriguing spy sent us the report that Major Pitcairn subsequently submitted in respect to the skirmish on
Lexington Green:

*Lt. Colonel Smith placed me in command of his advance party
and ordered me to press ahead of his column for the purpose
of securing the bridges at Concord and Sudbury. I selected two
hundred of the army's best marchers and set out three hours
before dawn.*

Before reaching the town of Lexington, a party of our scouts came to me with information they had gathered from a patriot captured earlier that night. I was therefore aware that a potentially sizeable force of colonial militia was gathering in the town.

I reached its outskirts as the dawn was breaking. Prior to entering it, I heard a drum beating somewhere within its precincts.

British Grenadiers marching to Concord [22]

Exchanging fire on Lexington Common on the morning of April 19, 1775 [23]

Interpreting this to be a call to arms, I halted and ordered my marines to load their muskets. Before we resumed our march, I instructed the men that on no account were they to fire without my orders.

Upon entering the town, I found approximately seventy armed provincials standing in a straggling line across its commons. I ordered my marines to face them and when they had done this, I called out to the men standing against us saying, "Disperse you rebels." When they did not do this, I repeated my order. "Damn you," I said, this time with some feeling, "Throw down your arms and disperse." I then ordered my men to advance.

As they did, four or five shots were fired from behind a wall on their right flank. Several more were fired from a Meeting House on their left. My men, being then enraged by the affront, returned this fire without my orders. The firing continued in that situation for some little time until I regained control of them. About this time, Colonel Smith arrived in the town. The Yankees having fled and order now restored, he ordered us to proceed on to Concord.

Major Pitcairn failed to mention that his redcoats killed eight of our compatriots and that their deaths were the first of the American Revolution.

The commander of the Concord militia was Colonel James Barrett. His son Amos, who was present that day, gave me this account of the battle at Concord Bridge.

The skirmish at Concord Bridge the morning of April 19, 1775 [24]

My father, Colonel James Barrett, was in command of the Concord minutemen on the day of the battle. Major John Buttrick was second-in-command. This is what happened, as I recall it:

We set out from Concord after midmorning on April 19. Our objective was to join the other militias that were gathering on Lexington Green. Having proceeded about a mile and half on the road to Lexington, we saw the redcoats coming toward us. My father and Major Buttrick held a brief council at this point and determined that we should keep ahead of them rather than to confront them. We did this by moving from ridge to ridge on their flank. When we reached the town, we withdrew through it to a safe distance on its far side. There my father held another council-of-war in which it was agreed that we would take a position across the North Bridge.

The British retreat following the Battles of Lexington and Concord [25]

Relocating there, we watched as the soldiers entered the town and began to search it. About this time, a company of light infantry came out from the town and took up a position at the foot of the south bridge. Seven more companies secured the north bridge.

The British found little in the way of hidden supplies in the town as we had removed them three days before on the advice of John Hancock. The few items they did find, they collected in the center of the town and burned.

Seeing the smoke from this fire, we concluded that they were burning the town. We then advanced from the ridge overlooking the river and approached the bridge that crossed it. As we approached, a nervous British sentry fired upon us.

This triggered a general exchange in which several men on both sides were slain.

These events seemed to confuse the British commander who dithered in the town for several more hours before giving the order to withdraw. The British began their retreat in the early afternoon.

Colonel Smith spent the rest of this long day marching back to Boston. During this time our militias showered a constant, often murderous fire upon his unfortunate subordinates.

Lt. Colonel Smith submitted his report, which our special spy copied, three days later. In it, he confirmed the difficulty he had reaching safety. Here is the part where he described it:

At Concord we found very few inhabitants in the town; those we met with both Major Pitcairn and myself took all possible pains to convince that we meant them no injury, and that if they opened their doors when required to search for military stores, not the slightest mischief would be done. We had opportunities of convincing them of our good intentions, but they were sulky; and one of them even struck Major Pitcairn.

On our leaving Concord to return to Boston, they began to fire on us from behind the walls, ditches, trees, etc., which, as we marched, increased to a very great degree, and continued without the intermission of five minutes altogether, for, I believe, upwards of eighteen miles; so that I can't think but it must have been a preconcerted scheme in them, to attack the King's troops the first favorable opportunity that offered, otherwise, I think they could not, in so short a time as from our marching out, have raised such a numerous body, and for so great a space of ground.

Notwithstanding the enemy's numbers, they did not make one gallant effort during so long an action, though our men were so very much fatigued, but kept under cover.

—Lieutenant Colonel Smith,
10th Regiment of Foot, to General Gage (April 22, 1775)

It was dark when Colonel Smith's men crossed the Charlestown Neck to safety under the guns of the warships in the Charles River. About twenty percent of the 1700 British soldiers who participated in the expedition were either killed, wounded, or lost. Our losses were comparatively small with 49 killed and about the same number wounded.

The greatest victim of the defeat that day was General Gage who now found himself and his army prisoners in Massachusetts's capital city.

The men who chased the Redcoats back to Boston formed a ring around the city. Over the coming weeks, their numbers grew to between sixteen and seventeen thousand men as patriots from across New England joined their ranks. They eventually came to be known as the "army of observation."

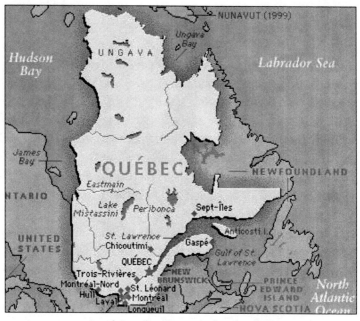

Royal Canadian Province of Quebec [26]

CHAPTER FOUR

The Siege of Boston: Part 2

The Excursion Up Lake Champlain

Ethan Allen captured Fort Ticonderoga before I joined General Washington's staff. Because this was important an important factor in the British decision to evacuate Boston, I have reconstructed what happened from reports I found in the archives.

CANADA ASSUMED a new importance to us after the war began, but even before that our patriotic leaders had been thinking about it. Some looked upon the former French province of Quebec as a sister to our thirteen English colonies. The 1st Continental Congress therefore invited the people of Quebec to send a delegation to the 2nd Congress when it convened in May of 1775. The letter was dated October 26, 1774.

This offer came to nothing, however, because most Canadians did not wish to be part of an American coalition. After the shots were fired at Lexington and Concord, we therefore began to look at the Province of Quebec with a suspicious eye. You can understand our concern by reading this short excerpt from a report that circulated in the 2nd Continental Congress at the time General Washington was elected to command the patriotic army:

> British Armies can attack the American colonies by ferrying up the St Lawrence and Richelieu Rivers from Quebec, then down Lake Champlain to Fort Crown Point and Fort Ticonderoga. From there it was an easy transit down the Hudson River to New York. By fortifying this military highway, the British can divide our New England members from those further south.

Trapped now in Boston, General Gage began making plans to do this. No sooner had his battered army reached shelter than General Gage sent a letter to Governor Sir Guy Carleton in Quebec instructing him to strengthen Fort Ticonderoga and Fort Crown Point.

Two daring patriots were also thinking about this. Ethan Allen was the notorious founder of the Green Mountain Boys in New Hampshire. Benedict Arnold was a hot-blooded merchant who lived in western Connecticut.

Allen and Arnold both understood the importance of the forts. Both men were aware that they held great quantities of valuable military stores (including more than fifty siege cannon) and that the forts had been allowed to deteriorate to the

Ethan Allen [27]

Colonel Benedict Arnold [28]

point where they were virtually indefensible. Both men were also hungry for fame and glory.

Ethan Allen had become familiar with Fort Ticonderoga and its circumstances while roaming through the Green Mountains. Benedict Arnold had gained similar knowledge while traveling back and forth between Montreal and his home in Connecticut.

In the hope of winning a field command, Benedict Arnold shared his idea of taking the fort with a colonel in the Connecticut Militia. This man, whose name was Silas Deane, passed Arnold's intelligence on to the Connecticut Committee of Safety. The members of this committee decided to capture the fort with volunteers they began to recruit in northwestern Connecticut, western Massachusetts and the New Hampshire Grants.

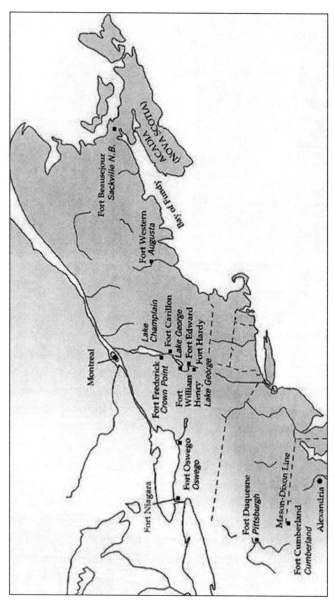

British Forts at the time of the American Revolution (Fort Carillon is the French name for Fort Ticonderoga) [29]

Fort Ticonderoga [30]

About this time, John Brown, an American spy from Pittsfield, brought the matter to the attention of Massachusetts's Committee of Safety. Thus, a month before shots were fired on Lexington Green, our leaders in Massachusetts had also concluded that Ticonderoga "must be seized as soon as possible should hostilities be committed by the King's Troops."

Not one let an opportunity to slip by, Benedict Arnold decided to present his plan to the Massachusetts Committee of Safety which was sitting then in Cambridge. Since Massachusetts was eager to have the guns and ammunition stored in the forts, the committee quickly approved his proposal. It gave him a colonel's commission and placed him in command of a "secret mission" to seize the fort. When he had done this, he was to send its military supplies to Cambridge. The Committee gave him 100 pounds to finance the mission and ordered him to begin immediately.

Ethan Allen plots the capture of Ticonderoga at Castleton [31]

While Colonel Arnold was raising his force in the western part of the colony, he learned that Ethan Allen was also preparing to attack on the fort. He immediately set off to overtake his self-appointed rival. Riding all night, Colonel Arnold reached Bennington in Vermont the following day. In the course of his interview with Ethan Allen, Colonel Arnold learned two things. First, he learned that Allen was ready to attack the fort. Second, he learned that Allen would neither surrender his own command nor serve under someone else. Seeing no alternative,

Ethan Allen leads the attack on May 10, 1775 [32]

Colonel Arnold agreed to be part of Allen's assault.

The following account is from the report Ethan Allen submitted to the Continental Congress after capturing the fort:

"On the night of May 9th, I loaded eighty men into the boats I had gathered on the east side of Lake Champlain and sailed the half mile to the fort.

An officer by the name of William Delaplace commanded the fort. Captain Delaplace was asleep at the early hour of the morning when I and my Green Mountain Boys crept through the fort's porous wall. Once inside, I seized the lone sentry standing watch and ordered him to lead me to the captain's quarters. My loud banging soon roused Captain Delaplace. He came to the door himself.

I then demanded that he surrender the fort. By what authority, Captain Delaplace wished to know, did I presume to issue an order to an officer of the King? I drew my sword and held it over his head. "In the name of the Great Jehovah and the Continental Congress!" I thundered back. I added that I would massacre the garrison if he did not immediately comply.

Ethan Allen demands the surrender of Fort Ticonderoga [33]

Dressing quickly in his chambers, Captain Delaplace returned with his sword and gave it to me. Fort Crown Point surrendered two days later."

About this time, three hundred of Colonel Arnold's men reached the fort. Having at last the greater number of men, Colonel Arnold took command. This did not sit well with the Green Mountain Boys. One of their officers went so far as to insult Colonel Arnold. Outraged by this insolence, Colonel Arnold challenged the man to a duel. Of this, he later said:

Cannon at Fort Ticonderoga [34]

"On refusing to draw like a gentleman, he having a [sword]
by his side and cases of loaded pistols in his pockets, I kicked
him very heartily and ordered him from the Post."

You will not be surprised to hear that Ethan Allen made
no mention of Colonel Benedict Arnold in his reports on the
capture of Fort Ticonderoga.

A Closer Look at Benedict Arnold

Since we have been speaking of Benedict Arnold, let us pause
for a moment and take a closer look at this infamous traitor.
Is there anyone more despised in America today than Benedict Arnold? I think not, yet he was one of the first to answer
the call to oust the British and the tyranny imposed by their

Benedict Arnold escapes to a British warship in the Hudson River [35]

distant king. Benedict Arnold's heroic contributions to the American cause before he became a traitor bear re-telling.

Here is a brief biography of the man that I found after the war:

> Benedict Arnold was commissioned as a Captain in the Governor's Second Company of Guards in Connecticut a month before the shots were fired on Lexington Green.
>
> When he heard the news, Captain Arnold set out with his company to join the battle. Arriving on the scene and finding that the fighting had already ended, he requested the Massachusetts Committee of Safety to give him permission to capture Ft. Ticonderoga. The committee consented, elevated Captain Arnold to the rank of Colonel and sent him to western Massachusetts to raise the troops he needed to accomplish the mission.

You know already that others had their eyes on that same objective—Ethan Allen and his Green Mountain Boys and the state of Connecticut. You also know that Colonel Arnold caught up with Allen at Bennington, that Allen refused to acknowledge Colonel Arnold's authority to command the expedition and that the attack on the fort was a success.

What is not readily understood is that Colonel Arnold was roundly disrespected by Allen's men, first among whom was Colonel Easton an officer from Massachusetts. This was the man who carried word of the victory back to the Massachusetts Committee of Safety. In his report, Easton did his best to disregard Colonel Arnold's role in the victory. This led the hot-tempered Colonel Arnold to challenge Easton to a duel— which he wisely refused.

A few days after the capture of Fort Ticonderoga, Colonel Arnold's men captured St. John's, Massachusetts. Justifiably proud of his accomplishments, when he reached home, Colonel Arnold asked for command of all Connecticut's military forces. He did not understand that in making this request he crossed an invisible line from war into politics. More specifically, Colonel Arnold did not understand that Connecticut's committee of safety saw itself in competition with Massachusetts's committee of safety for the credit of capturing Ft. Ticonderoga. Since Colonel Arnold had acted on the authority of the Massachusetts committee, the Connecticut committee refused to give him command of their troops. This created a grievance that festered in the colonel's teaming mind.

Colonel Arnold paid most of the expenses of his troops on this expedition. The Massachusetts Committee of Safety which had authorized it, agreed to reimburse the colonel for only a small portion of his expenditures. Eventually he submitted his account to the Continental Congress which paid the balance.

During this lingering controversy, Colonel Arnold's military accomplishments came to the attention of General Washington who recognized his great promise. When Colonel Arnold met with General Washington, he proposed that a strike be made on Quebec. General Washington agreed and gave him command of 1,100 troops to undertake the project.

Colonel Arnold began his expedition through the heartland of Maine in mid-September.

Despite the desertion of Colonel Enos, his battalion and critical quantities of food and ammunition, Colonel Arnold reached Quebec in mid-November. His losses were so great, however, that he decided against a frontal attack. Instead he retired to Pointe aux Trembles where he was joined by General Montgomery. You will learn how poor General Montgomery and ill-fated Colonel Arnold fared in their attack on Quebec in my next story. Suffice it to say here that it was Colonel Arnold who brought the defeated American army home.

During this retreat, Colonel Arnold was promoted to Brigadier General. In the summer of 1776, he paused to build a fleet of ships on the shores of Lake Champlain. In October of that year, he intercepted a British squadron which carried Sir Guy Carleton and an army he had assembled to invade the American colonies. Although he was completely overmatched in men and guns, Colonel Arnold repulsed Carleton's armada. Because he effectively destroyed Arnold's makeshift fleet, Sir Guy claimed victory. He then returned to Montreal to regroup and refit.

General Horatio Gates [36]   General Charles Lee [36a]

While Colonel Arnold was seizing every opportunity to fight the enemy, several of his fellow officers were plotting to remove his commanding general and take over his army. The leaders of this treachery were Horatio Gates and Charles Lee.

These treacherous men made General Arnold, a man General Washington had come to trust, one of their targets. While they were hatching their plot during the fall of 1776 and winter of 1777, the Congress was developing a list of new Major Generals. It should come as no surprise that Benedict Arnold was not on this list. The men who were—Lincoln, Mifflin, Stirling, St. Clair, and Stephens—were all junior in rank to General Arnold and inferior to him in terms of their accomplishments on behalf of the Patriot cause.

In April of 1776, a British force of 2,000 men attacked Danbury, Connecticut with the intent of destroying the military supplies we had collected there. General Wooster defended it with 600 men, but his force was not strong enough to repulse the attack. General Arnold was in nearby New Haven.

When the news reached him, he called out the militia and raced to Danbury to assist in the town's defense. He had two horses shot from under him, but succeeded in driving the British from the field.

As his reputation grew, it became impossible to deny General Arnold promotion to the rank of Major General. The date of his promotion, however, made him junior to the men who had been named to the rank in February.

Soon after General Arnold's belated promotion, General Washington received word that British armies under Generals Burgoyne and St. Leger were descending the Mohawk Valley. This was desperate news as it marked the first phase of the grand British plan to divide the colonies. If General Burgoyne managed to link with General Clinton in New York, they would separate New England from the southern colonies and be able to deal with them separately. General Washington responded by dispatching a force under General Arnold. Through a brilliant maneuver, General Arnold scattered St. Leger's army. He then joined Major General Horatio Gates who commanded a second colonial army against General Burgoyne.

Gates and Burgoyne parried with each other for several days. Then at Freeman's Farm near Saratoga, General Arnold stopped a sudden British thrust. He might have destroyed the British army had General Gates sent the reinforcements he requested, but instead of providing the needed reserves, General Gates ordered the withdrawal of a segment of General Arnold's force.

So incensed was Arnold, that he turned his attention to his superior. A violent argument ensued in which General Gates ordered General Arnold to leave the field. Refusing to abandon his men, General Arnold rushed back into the center of the fight and took personal command of the left side of the American line. The right side of the line he placed under the command of Nathaniel Greene who was supported by Daniel Morgan and his Virginia riflemen. During these critical moments, General Gates was not on the field.

General Arnold's inspired leadership turned the tide of the battle, but as it reached its turbulent peak, General Arnold was wounded again in the leg (as he had been during the ill-fated invasion of Quebec). While he was recovering after the stirring American victory, General Gates proclaimed himself the "Hero of Saratoga". The Congress was not fooled, however. In January 1778, it antedated General Arnold's commission as Major General and restored his seniority in the service.

In June of 1778, as General Arnold recovered from this latest wound, General Washington placed him in command of Philadelphia. It was here that he met Margaret Shippen. The two were soon engaged. Subsequently they married. Unfortunately for Benedict Arnold, his beloved wife was a Tory sympathizer and over the next two years she undermined his commitment to the patriotic cause. She was assisted by many small affronts delivered by men who envied him. Various charges were brought against him by these men of lesser ability. Although General Arnold regularly survived the congressional investigations these charged provoked, they eroded his faith in the political leaders of his newborn country.

Being surrounded by Tories and being married to one took its toll on Benedict Arnold. Through them he became acquainted with John Andre, a charming man, a British officer—and a spy. In July of 1780, General Arnold approached General Washington with a request. Could he complete his convalescence as the commander of West Point? General Washington acquiesced, not imagining that his trusted subordinate was plotting with Major Andre to surrender the fort to the British.

General Arnold's plan unraveled, however. Three New York militia men had hidden near the road Andre' chose to travel in hopes of catching Tory cattle thieves. When they stopped Major Andre', they found incriminating papers in one of his boots.

When General Arnold learned of this, he fled from West Point to New York City. Overnight the great American hero became a loathsome traitor. Ignoring his treachery, the British made him a Brigadier General and in early 1781 sent him to pillage Virginia. Later that same year, he led an attack in Connecticut which the British hoped would divert Washington from marching south to meet Cornwallis.

In each of his assignments as a British commander, Benedict Arnold showed the same daring and ability he had exhibited as an American. After the war, he and his wife settled in St. Johns, New Brunswick, but by 1791 they were living in London. He died in 1801, a bitter and remorseful man—truly a man without a country. Had he died in battle at Ticonderoga, or at Quebec, or at Saratoga, or at Danbury, or on Lake Champlain, he would have been remembered as one of our greatest heroes. How strange fate is!

HMS Cerberus at anchor in Boston Harbor [37]

CHAPTER FIVE

The Siege of Boston: Part 3

Bunker Hill

After the disastrous mission to Concord, General Gage retained authority long enough to make one more colossal blunder. This one he did not make alone however. HMS *Cerberus* reached Boston on May 25, 1775. On it were his three new generals: William Howe, Henry Clinton and John Burgoyne.

One witty versifier celebrated the event with a rhyme that went like this:

> *Behold the Cerberus the Atlantic plough,*
> *Her precious cargo, Burgoyne, Clinton, Howe.*
> *Bow, wow, wow!*

General William Howe [38]

General Henry Clinton [39]

I N EARLY JUNE, General Gage held a council-of-war with the newly arrived generals of his army. In this meeting, they all agreed that two strategic positions on the city's outer perimeter should be fortified. These were Bunker Hill and the Dorchester Heights. They agreed to begin by taking up positions on Bunker Hill on June 18.

General John Burgoyne [40]

One of the first acts of the Massachusetts Committee of Safety had been to appoint Artemus Ward commander of the colony's militias. When spies informed the committee that

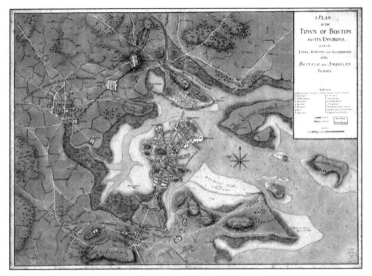

A Plan of the Town of Boston [41]

General Gage planned to man the earthworks he had constructed on Bunker Hill to shield his army after its retreat from Concord, it ordered General Ward to occupy and expand these fortifications. Because General Ward was busy gathering powder and shot, he delegated the task to Israel Putnam.

On the night of June 16, General Putnam and Colonel William Prescott led twelve hundred men across the Charlestown Neck and began to expand the trenches on the crests of Bunker Hill and Breed's Hill.

While surveying the ground on the morning of the 17th, General Howe espied the colonials at work on the two hills. Hastily convening another council-of-war, he and his colleagues agreed that the fortifications should be assailed while

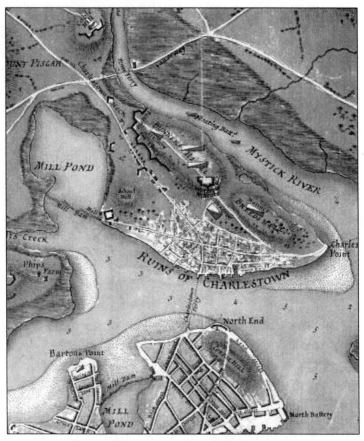

Section: A Plan for the Town of Boston [42]

they were minimal. I later found General Clinton's account of this council. In part, he said:

> *"The hill being open and easy of ascent could easily be carried by a frontal assault. In this we all agreed. General Howe, being senior among us, was given command of the assault.*

Colonel William Prescott [43]

He immediately commenced to ferry the troops across the Charles River to the foot of Moulton's Hill at the east end of the Charlestown peninsula. Once he had formed them into lines, he launched his attack."

Here is an account of the battle given to me shortly after I arrived in Cambridge by one of General Putnam's men:

General Putnam watched the British advance with cold determination. Knowing that his army was low on ammunition, he

Atop Bunker Hill [44]

Three bristling red lines advanced up the hill toward our trenches [45]

The death of General Warren [46]

issued his famous order to Colonel Prescott. *"Don't shoot,"* he instructed, *"until you see the whites of their eyes."*

Three bristling red lines advanced up the hill toward our trenches. The first was but a few yards in front of us when Colonel Prescott finally gave the order to fire. So great was the slaughter that they all buckled. Now we fired at will. Under this relentless barrage, the survivors of the failed assault fled back down the blood-soaked slope.

At the base of the hill, as the warships in the Charles River pounded our position, they formed again. These new lines then started up the hill.

Again we waited to see the whites of their eyes and as before, we dealt them a terrible blow. Refusing to be defeated, their commander formed his lines a third time. This time our ammunition gave out and the Redcoats carried the hill. Among

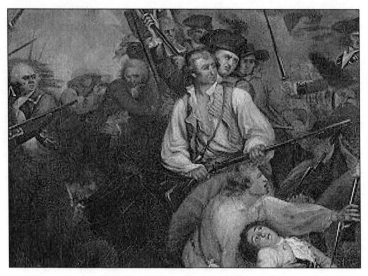

Major General Israel Putnam at the Battle of Bunker Hill (far left) [47]

the last to leave the crumbling line was Dr. Joseph Warren, a founder of the patriotic movement and leading member of the Massachusetts Committee of Safety. He fell in a final heroic effort to protect his retreating compatriots.

Thus did the British win the day. It was a hollow victory though. General Howe suffered a thousand casualties including the deaths of ninety two of his officers. So great was this loss he made no further attempt to break our siege.

Remembering a Connecticut Patriot

As the commander of our Continental Army was a heroic Virginian we sometimes overlook the men of the northern colonies to who commanded in the field. General Nathanael

Greene, for example, who later commanded our forces in the south, was from Rhode Island. Here, I will remember a Patriot from Connecticut.

Long before we took arms to win political independence, some of our brave men answered the call to defend the western frontiers against the French and their Indian allies. Israel Putnam first distinguished himself in this conflict.

Israel Putnam was born on January 7, 1718 in Massachusetts, the tenth of eleven children. As he approached manhood he realized that if he received anything from his father it would not be enough to support him. He therefore set about making himself self sufficient. Not long after marrying, which he did at age twenty, he joined his brother-in-law in purchasing 500 acres of land in Connecticut where land was cheaper. Within a short time he bought his brother-in-law's share of this land. He then took charge in developing a profitable business raising apples and sheep.

Control over the continent was still in dispute at that time. Young Israel's sympathies were—understandably—with England and against France. When the French threatened to invade New York, he therefore volunteered his services. He was given a Captaincy under General Phineas Lynch. From 1754 through 1758 he served as a ranger. In this time, he advanced to the rank of major.

In one harrowing episode, he was captured by an Indian war party. His captors bound him to a stake and were preparing to burn him alive when a French officer appeared. This merciful man persuaded Major Putnam's Indian executioners to spare him. The French later freed him in a prisoner exchange. Shortly after that he was promoted to Lt Colonel.

After the French and Indian war he joined his old commander, General Lyman, in an expedition to the West Indies. In 1764, he was promoted to the rank of Colonel and given command of a Connecticut regiment being mustered into the British army under General Bradstreet.

He left active service at the end of 1764 and returned to his farm. Soon after that his loving wife died leaving him with 10 children. He remarried the following year. Now a time of peace, he focused on his family and farming.

When the conflict with Parliament proved unresolvable, Israel Putnam sided with those who favored independence. News of the events at Lexington and Concord reached him while he was plowing in his fields. Without a second thought, he leaped onto his horse and rode through night to Cambridge. When he presented himself the following morning, he was appointed brigadier general and placed in command of the forces gathering in the town. Commander of the colonial militias at Bunker Hill, he was among the last to evacuate when they exhausted their ammunition.

After the battle, General Howe paid him an unheard of compliment by offering him a commission as a Major General in the British Army. Suffice it to say, he rejected the offer. A few days later General Washington offered him a similar commission in the patriotic army. This offer he accepted.

The following year, General Washington gave him command of 5000 men guarding New York. This force was overwhelmed by the British army when it descended upon the city in 1777. General Putnam fought bravely at Harlem Heights and Fort Washington and in other engagements during the battle for New York. While posted at Fishkill, his second wife died, which was a grievous loss to him.

Later in 1779, while posted near West Point, he suffered a stroke which forced him to retire from the army. He lived eleven more years—long enough to see the former colonies ratify the Constitution of United States of America.

General Washington takes command of the Continental Army [48]

CHAPTER SIX

The Siege of Boston: Part 4

Dorchester Heights

General Washington directed that I prepare this report of the events leading up to the British evacuation of Boston and their subsequent flight to Halifax.

THE MILITIAMEN who filled the camps around Boston were volunteers who could go home whenever they pleased. Aware of the danger this posed to the patriotic cause, the Massachusetts Provincial Congress voted to raise an army of 26 regiments. The legislatures in New Hampshire, Rhode Island, and Connecticut did the same although they proposed to raise smaller forces.

On June 14, 1775, the Congress in Philadelphia followed the lead of these legislatures by voting to establish a Continental Army to defend all the colonies. It was to be formed

Continental Army recruits training [49]

from the forces already in place and through recruitment of ten additional companies of riflemen from Pennsylvania, Maryland, and Virginia. These were to be "flying camps" of light infantries. Soldiers in the new Continental Army would enlist for terms of one year.

On June 15, the Congress voted unanimously to appoint George Washington to be the army's Commander-in-Chief. Though fearful of the responsibility he would have and the likelihood that he would fail, he agreed to serve. General now of an army, he set out to take command.

General Washington reached Cambridge on July 3, 1775. Not surprisingly, the army he found there was of dubious quality. It consisted of a rag tag collection of farmers and merchants having neither discipline, nor order, nor government. They wore clothing having no uniformity and many of them carried weapons that could not be used in battle. Worse, when they grew bored, they went home.

By the end of the year, this exodus had significantly reduced the army's size. These losses were partially offset by the men from Massachusetts, New Hampshire, Connecticut and Rhode Island all of whom had enlisted for twelve months. By the beginning of the New Year, General Washington had organized them into three divisions, six brigades, and thirty eight regiments. January 1, 1776 can therefore be fixed as the birth day of our Continental Army.

While he brought his army into fighting order, General Washington considered what to do with the Dorchester Heights. They were important because they commanded both the city of Boston and the harbor through which it received its supplies.

General Washington's most pressing concern was to prepare his army of villagers to fight England's professional soldiers. By day, he drilled his troops. By night he pleaded with the Continental Congress to send more arms and clothing.

General Washington's spies kept him informed of the deteriorating conditions in Boston. Small pox was rampant and food was in short supply. Re-supply was possible only by sea. If this avenue were closed, General Howe would have either to fight or evacuate the city. While General Washington considered the prospects, a new flag was raised over the Continental Army. It contained elements reminiscent of our colonial connection to Britain. These included a miniature Union Jack, crosses of St. Andrew and St. George. Its thirteen red and white stripes left no doubt, however, that it was an "America" flag.

General Washington had two alternatives. He could attack the city from across the Charles River. Or, if he mounted cannon Dorchester Heights, he could close the port and shut off

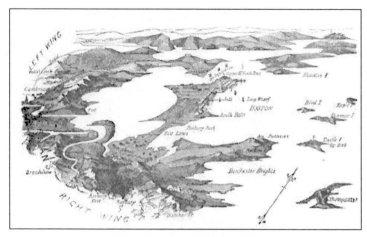

Map of the Siege of Boston [50]

the city's last line of supply. In this case, General Howe might well evacuate the city. In December, he called a council-of-war to decide the matter. I was there and heard no one speak in favor of crossing the Charles.

Portly Henry Knox now enters our story.

The following account of his heroic enterprise was published by Benjamin Edes in his *Boston Gazette* shortly after the British evacuated the city:

Before the war, Henry Knox was a bookseller in our city. He joined the militia after the battles of Lexington and Concord and served under General Putnam at the Battle of Bunker Hill. He then joined the Continental Army as it was recruited under General Washington. During this time, he met and impressed the general who appointed him a colonel and offered him command of the army's artillery.

72

Colonel Henry Knox [51]

Knox suggested to General Washington that it could be concluded by retrieving the guns from Fort Ticonderoga and mounting them on Dorchester Heights. General Washington immediately approved the idea and ordered Colonel Know to implement it.

Colonel Knox made his way north to Lake Champlain through the December snow. At Ticonderoga he loaded fifty nine cannon from Forts Ticonderoga and Crown Point onto ox-drawn sleds and began the trek south. He followed the west bank of the Hudson River to Albany. Crossing there, he proceeded east over the snowy Berkshire Mountains. Continuing

73

*on toward Boston at a pace of five miles per day, he com-
pleted the 300 mile expedition in fifty six days arriving in
Cambridge on January 24, 1776.*

This account was given to me by Sergeant Richard Hudnut
who served under Colonel Knox on the mission:

*Shortly after General Washington took command of the army,
he appointed Henry Knox chief of the army's artillery and
gave him the rank of Colonel. The first problem Colonel Knox
faced as commander of the army's artillery was that the army
had no artillery. He was aware, however, that Colonel Benedict Arnold of Connecticut and Ethan Allen and his Green
Mountain Boys had captured Fort Ticonderoga in May. He
therefore proposed to bring its guns to Boston and General
Washington authorized him to do so.*

*I had been with Colonel Arnold when he seized the decrepit
fort and was familiar with the trails twixt Ticonderoga and
Boston. When I presented my credentials to Colonel Knox, he
eagerly accepted my offer to guide the expedition and made
me his chief of scouts.*

*It was now the month of December and the harshness of
winter was upon us. Nevertheless, we pressed on and in good
time reached Fort George which lay about a mile below Ticonderoga. At this point, Colonel Knox asked that I join him
in his quarters to plan the recovery of the cannon and mortars which we would do on the following day. As we warmed
ourselves before the fire, a sentry ushered in a captured British officer. His name was John Andre and he proved a most
delightful fellow—difficult it was for me to believe that was
our enemy.*

Colonel Knox's "noble train of artillery" [52]

The city of Boston as seen from Dorchester Heights [53]

We reached the fort early the following morning. To the Colonel's delight, we found some 59 cannon of various poundage including howitzers and mortars. We also found a goodly supply of powder and shot. Altogether we collected some 60 tonnes of material. As we gathered it, Colonel Knox engaged several local fishermen and their boats to ferry us across Lake George for our journey back to Cambridge.

Having loaded the arms and ammunition, the sleds, the oxen and the men onto these vessels, we set off. The ground was snow covered, but the lake had not yet frozen. We were therefore able to break the ice near the shoreline and gain access to open water. Then it was that adversity set in. The wind was so strong that it drove one of our boats onto a shoal. It died down enough for us to free the heavily laden vessel, but once we had accomplished this, it regained its former strength and fury.

We strove against it for the greatest part of the day, but finally made the far shore. We then transferred the arms and

Manning Dorchester Heights [54]

powder to the sleds and began the overland part of the journey. Our path led over snow-covered hills and across frozen streams. Our progress was slow, however, because our sleds often became mired in the little-used trails we traversed. In this tedious way, we pushed across the Berkshires and through the forests of central Massachusetts. We did not reach Cambridge until the middle of January.

The journey Colonel Knox expected to take two weeks had taken ten, but General Washington's army now had the artillery it needed to end the siege of Boston.

General Washington began his move onto the Dorchester Heights soon after Colonel Knox's return. His first step was

Gun placements on Dorchester Heights [55]

to create a diversion. He began by bombarding the city of Boston on the night of March 2nd with batteries he placed on Lechmere's Point on Cobble Hill near Cambridge and on Lamb's Dam in Roxbury. The following night, he repeated this cannonade.

General John Thomas describes what happened next:

On the night of March 4, the batteries to the west of the city again opened fire. This time, however, they covered the movement of two thousand of my men onto the Heights.

We carried with us trenching tools and, working feverishly, we completed in a single night a system of earthworks that looked down upon the city and the harbor. General Washington watched approvingly as we brought his fortifications into

The evacuation of Boston [56]

form. Facing bombardment from this new installation, we all understood that General Howe would have to fight or flee. In the event he attempted to storm our new fortifications on the city's southern perimeter, General Washington was prepared to attack the city from the west through Cambridge.

At sunrise on March 5, we looked out upon the city from behind a battery of heavy cannon. A few days later we moved more guns to Nook's Hill which was closer still to the enemy. The British could not overcome our advantage as they could not elevate the muzzles of their cannon to fire above the empty side of our hill.

We had now encircled General Howe and his army. Our cannon could reach every corner of the city and the harbor. General Washington called the council several times over the following days seeking support for his plan to drive the

British into the sea, but each time the decision was to continue the siege.

We did not wait long for General Howe to make his move. On March 17, he loaded his army and his Tory supporters onto ships and retreated to safety in Nantasket Harbor. Ten days later, in a fleet that numbered 170 ships, he and his minions sailed on to Halifax.

We did not know it at the time, but all the while General Washington was laying his plans to fortify Dorchester Heights, General Howe was preparing to evacuate the city. His superior in London, Lord Dartmouth, had by then concluded that the war had a larger dimension and had instructed General Howe to move "some place southward." General Howe's evacuation was a success. We found few stores of equipment in the city when we took possession of it on March 18. That General Howe did not burn it upon his departure is a testament to the humanity of the man.

The lofty cliffs of Quebec seen from across the St Lawrence River in winter [57]

CHAPTER SEVEN

Misadventure in Canada

General Montgomery and Colonel Arnold are sent to capture Quebec

I will introduce the lamentable story of our "liberation" of Canada by quoting from two addresses issued by our 2nd Continental Congress.

ON MAY 26, our Congress announced to the people of America that Great Britain's aggression at Concord and Lexington marked the beginning of the war. Soon after this, it sent an address to the people of Great Britain which explained our sentiments:

"Shall the descendants of Britons tamely submit to this? No, sirs! We never will. While we revere the memory of our gallant and virtuous ancestors, we never can surrender those glorious privileges for which they fought, bled, and conquered. Your fleets may destroy our towns, and ravage

our sea-coasts. These are not inconsiderable objects, but they are of no moment to men whose bosoms glow with the ardor of liberty. We can retire beyond the reach of your navy, and without any sensible diminution of the necessaries of life. There we will have the luxury of being free."

It added this in an address to the people of Ireland:

"Blessed with an indissoluble union, with a variety of internal resources, and with a firm reliance on the justice of the Supreme Disposer of all human events, we have no doubt of rising superior to all the machinations of evil and abandoned Ministers. We already anticipate the golden period, when liberty, with all the gentle arts of peace and humanity, shall establish her mild dominion in this western world, and erect eternal monuments to the memory of those virtuous patriots and martyrs, who shall have fought and bled and suffered in her cause."

In this defiant yet hopeful frame of mind, the Congress authorized the liberation of Canada. This was necessary, it decided, to deprive the Royal Navy and the British Army of a base for military operations against our thirteen American colonies.

On June 27, 1775 the Congress elected one of its own members to be one of the army's five new Major Generals. It now authorized General Philip Schuyler to develop a plan to seize Quebec. General Schuyler sent the Congress this summary of his plan shortly after accepting the assignment:

Philip Schuyler [58]   *Major General Philip Schuyler* [59]

*I shall gather and train an army at Fort Ticonderoga with all
practicable speed. Once it is fit to take the field, I shall lead
it up Lake Champlain and down the Richelieu River, pausing
long enough in my descent to seize the garrison and military
supplies at St Jean. I shall then turn west and take possession
of Montreal. When I have done this, I shall proceed down the
St Lawrence River and storm Quebec.*

While the Congress reviewed General Schuyler's plan,
General Washington made his way to Boston to take command of the army there. On June 25, he stopped for a brief
visit in New York City. During this visit he appointed Richard Montgomery, an officer who had retired from the British
army to farm in upstate New York, to be General Schuyler's
deputy commander.

Champlain-Richelieu Watershed [60]

As General Schuyler and General Montgomery made their preparations, General Washington met in Cambridge with Colonel Arnold. After conferring with Colonel Arnold, General Washington agreed to dispatch a second force under his command.

Colonel Arnold's plan was as follows:

I will recruit a force of volunteers from the army that presently sits idle around Boston. I will march from Cambridge

Brigadier General Richard Montgomery [61]

to Newburyport. There I will board schooners and sail to the Kennebec River which I will ascend to Fort Western. At Fort Western, I will transfer my men and supplies to bateaux and proceed upriver to the Great Carrying Place. I will portage to the Dead River and ascend it to the Height of Land. I will cross the Maine Highland to the Chaudière River which I shall then descend to Port Levi. There I will collect the army, cross

Colonel Benedict Arnold [62]

*the St Lawrence and rendezvous with General Schuyler before
the city of Quebec. Our two armies will launch a coordinated
assault and easily take the lightly defended city.*

General Schuyler met briefly with General Montgomery
in Albany in early July. From there he traveled on to Ticonderoga where he began to organize his army.

General Montgomery remained in Albany for another
month completing logistical arrangements then joined his
superior on Lake Champlain. After conferring with General

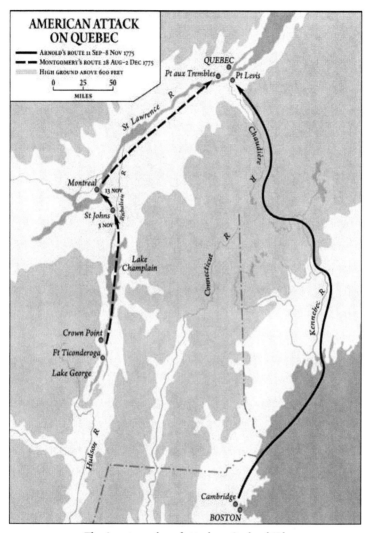

The American plan of attack on Quebec [63]

Fort Crown Point—Model [64]

The embarkation of Montgomery's troops at Crown Point [65]

Schuyler at Ticonderoga, General Montgomery proceeded to Fort Crown Point.

While General Schuyler drilled his troops, General Montgomery recruited a company of scouts and collected a flotilla to carry the invasion force up Lake Champlain. They were ready to sail by the end of August. The army they would lead into Canada consisted of 1700 men.

On the eve of their departure, General Schuyler's health suddenly failed. He then transferred command to his subordinate and returned home.

As I have already noted, General Montgomery's invasion route led past Fort St Jean.

Among the dispatches General Montgomery sent back to Congress were these:

Late October: On the Richelieu River before Fort St Jean

We have established a position before Fort St Jean which is Britain's southern-most outpost in Canada. This morning I ordered cannon placed on the north side of the town. While my troops were setting these guns, a messenger from Montreal stumbled into their midst. The dispatch he carried was signed by Governor Sir Guy Carleton himself and instructed the commander of the garrison, Major Charles Preston, to hold at all costs.

1 November: Before Fort St Jean
At Midday—

I ordered my artillerists to commence firing at dawn this morning. The garrison responded, but their feeble fire did not disturb us. We are doing considerable damage to their

Champlain Valley (1777) [66]

fortifications. I expect we are doing equal damage to the morale of their defenders.

After sundown

We continued the bombardment through the day. At sundown I ordered a cease fire and sent a message to Major Preston demanding that the garrison be surrendered upon pain of the city's destruction.

Fort-Saint-Jean [67]

Firing on Fort St Jean [68]

Montreal [69]

The Isles of Montreal [70]

The surrender of Montreal [71]

Fortress Quebec [72]

A view of the Citadel of Quebec [73]

Quebec City Walls [74]

3 November: Fort St Jean

Yesterday at four o'clock I accepted the surrender of the fort and the town. Major Preston transferred these facilities into my possession this morning. I will send the surrendered personnel and the supplies that are not useful to my mission to Fort Ticonderoga tomorrow morning. Once they are underway, I shall leave a small garrison here and proceed to Montreal.

12 November: Before Montreal

I have established a line in front of this island city and have issued an ultimatum to Sir Guy Carleton demanding his surrender on pain of the city's destruction.

13 November: Montreal
About Sundown—

Montreal surrendered at midday today without firing a shot. I took possession of the city prior to sundown. While I was engaged in the negotiations for the city's surrender, Sir Guy managed to slip away in a small fleet that carried the greatest number of the city's defenders.

19 November: On the St Lawrence between Montreal and Quebec

I am pleased to inform your excellencies that today I captured the fleet Governor Carleton used to make his escape from Montreal. Regrettably, Sir Guy again eluded capture. We will meet soon however as my army has boarded his ships and will proceed to Quebec at sunrise tomorrow.

Situated on a towering bluff overlooking the St Lawrence River, Quebec had become a virtually impregnable fortress. The inland face of the city was protected by massive fortifications.

Its citadel dominated the St Lawrence Seaway.

Facing such a formidable military obstacle, General Montgomery elected to wait for Colonel Arnold to join him before launching an attack. But where was Colonel Arnold?

Colonel Arnold traveled upriver from Fort Western in a canoe [75]

CHAPTER EIGHT

Arnold's Ill-fated Expedition

Colonel Arnold's expedition across the highlands of Maine was one of the most brazen undertakings of the war. I am going to tell you the story using the words of the men who participated in it.

O N THE MORNING of September 11, 1775 Colonel Arnold departed from Cambridge with 1100 men. Three days later his army boarded schooners at Newburyport, Massachusetts and sailed one hundred mile up the coast of Maine to the mouth of Kennebec River. It proceeded thirty miles up the Kennebec River to Fort Western, which is now called Augusta.

I received this account of the expedition from Colonel Aaron Burr who served on General Washington's staff during our retreat from New York:

Colonel Arnold planned to complete the passage from Fort Western to Quebec in twenty days. He based his calculation

Map published by Henry Delahoy Symonds of New England in 1795 [76]

Map Key: A: Cambridge, Massachusetts; B: Newburyport, Massachusetts;
C: Fort Western; D: Fort Halifax; E: Lower end of the Great Carrying Place;
F: Height of Land between the Kennebec and the Chaudière River drainages;
G: Lake Mégantic

Colonel Aaron Burr [77]

on information contained in a map he received from General Washington prior to his departure.

The map Colonel Arnold used was drawn fifteen years earlier by a British military engineer by the name of John Montresor. Unknown to either General Washington or Colonel Arnold, it had been altered by a loyalist who meant to obstruct a possible American passage through Maine to Quebec. The map indicated, for example, that the distance between Fort Western and Quebec was 180 miles. It was actually 300 miles. Nor did it show Spider Lake or the vast swamp that occupies the area on its southern perimeter. Important route markings were also missing.

The map General Washington provided to Colonel Benedict Arnold [78]

Paddling up the Kennebec River [79]

On September 24, at Fort Western, we loaded our supplies into six-man bateaux built specially to carry us upriver. Colonel Arnold traveled in a canoe which he paddled in and out of our convoy issuing orders and giving the army encouragement. We pressed on against the current for a week during which time we passed Winslow and Skowhegan.

On October 2, we reached Norridgewock Falls. Here Colonel Arnold ordered a halt so that we could recover our strength before tackling the difficult ascent over the falls that disturbed the upper course of the river. We remained at Norridgewock Falls for a week waiting for the weather to clear. On October 9, the weather having finally cleared, Colonel Arnold ordered the advance to resume.

On October 11, we reached the Great Carrying Place and began the portage to Dead River.

Working against the flood on Dead River [80]

A violent storm erupted soon after we entered the twelve mile wasteland that separates the beginning point from the ending point of this strenuous passage. This storm turned much of the bog through which we plodded into frigid lakes. A formidable number of our company sickened and died as we waded through these lakes. Large quantities of food and powder were also destroyed. As our food gave out, desertions increased. It was in these grim moments that Colonel Enos's fourth division, lacking sustenance, turned back.

By October 15, the surviving units of our army had completed this grueling transit. Having collected what remained of our supplies and loaded them into our remaining bateaux, we set again to paddling, this time on the upper reach of Dead River. This work was made more difficult when more heavy rains flooded the river. Most of our remaining supplies were spoilt at this time.

Whitewater on the Chaudiere River [81]

Several boats were lost descending the Chaudiere River [82]

On October 25, our advance party finally crossed the Height of Land into Canada. It was here that Colonel Arnold's map began to deceive us. As it did not show Spider Lake or the swamp that preceded it, many detachments became lost. During these desperate days Colonel Dearborn's poor dog was eaten.

On October 31, the army was at last ready to descend the Chaudière River. Several boats were wrecked in the course of this passage because of the violence of the river. I did not personally witness their destruction because Colonel Arnold asked my cousin and myself to carry a letter forward to General Montgomery. Since we would travel through 120 miles of enemy territory, we disguised ourselves as Catholic priests— and prayed that our French would be good enough to fool the Canadians we could not avoid. Fortunately it was.

I have compiled this account of the events preceding General Montgomery's attack on Quebec from the general's log:

November 15: On the St Lawrence above Quebec

A pair of forlorn priests arrived in camp this afternoon. These proved to be Colonel Arnold's men, Aaron Burr and Mathias Ogden by name. That they survived Colonel Arnold's Maine crossing and their subsequent adventure through the wilds of Canada marks them, I suspect, for great things.

Colonel Arnold and his army arrived at Point Levis on November 9. On November 13, he crossed the St Lawrence River and established his army before the gates of Quebec. The following day he sent a message to Sir Guy Carleton demanding the surrender of the city. Colonel Arnold waited five days during which time he received no response from Governor Carleton. Since he had no means of enforcing his demand, he withdrew then eighteen miles upriver to Pointe-aux-Trembles. There on December 2 he joined his force, reduced now to only 500 men, to my own and relinquished his command.

After refitting Colonel Arnold's destitute men with equipment from the ships I captured from Sir Guy, we resumed our advance to Quebec. We reached the city on December 7 and placed it under siege. I then issued my own ultimatum for its surrender.

The British governor had used the time since his escape to prepare his capital to resist our assault. Confident in his strength, he made no response to my demand.

I waited before the city two weeks. Now time was running out. The enlistments of most of my men would begin to expire at the beginning of the new year and they would surely return home. Facing this dire prospect, I decided to launch a surprise attack on New Year's Eve.

The following account of the attack was given in a report by General Montgomery's second in command, Lt. Colonel Donald Campbell:

At 2:00 a.m. on December 31, 1775 General Montgomery ordered that muster be sounded throughout the camp. When the army was assembled, General Montgomery selected three hundred men to accompany him along the river path to the lower gate in the city's south wall. I was the second in command of this force.

Sir Guy Carleton reviewing troops at Quebec [83]

Colonel Arnold and Captain Morgan were to lead six hundred more men to the lower gate of the city's north wall. Having secured Lower Town, our combined forces would force the inner gate to the upper city and complete its capture.

Regrettably, when we began our attack we did not know that a deserter had divulged our plan to Governor Carleton.

As we assembled in the plain before the city, a watch officer within the city saw our lanterns and sounded the alarm. The garrison of the city stood to arms just as General Montgomery fired his signal rockets to start the attack. On the signal, our Canadians commenced a series of diversionary demonstrations.

The death of General Montgomery on December 31, 1775 [84]

Our advance along the river was hampered by snowdrifts and by great blocks of ice that had accumulated under the Cape Diamond Bastion. After surmounting these, we came to the first of several barricades at the edge of Lower Town. When we had cleared these, we could see the lights of the town. At this moment, General Montgomery, who led our column, shouted "Quebec is ours!" and charged ahead. These proved to be the general's last words.

A heavy snow was falling as General Montgomery led us into the town. Because of this, he did not observe that the house at the head of the street on which he advanced had been fortified. As we came up to it, the guard inside fired a cannon loaded with grapeshot. General Montgomery was killed instantly as were several others near him.

Canadian militiamen and British soldiers repulse the American assault at Rue Sault-au-Matelot [85]

Being now in command, I ordered the men near me to storm the house. At this critical moment, I discovered that the falling snow had rendered our muskets useless. Seeing no prospect for success without our weapons, I ordered a retreat."*

The following account of Colonel Arnold's attack was prepared by the colonel during his convalescence after the battle:

General Montgomery's attack through the south gate failed before I began my attack. I too was delayed by drifting snow and even lost a cannon in a snow-filled ditch. Despite these obstructions, I entered the town without difficulty. Once inside the city walls, however, I became lost in its maze of

___

* Web Source: http://canadachannel.ca/HCO/index.php/2._Battles_of_the_American_Revolution

Margaret Kemble Gage [86]

warehouses, docks and blind alleys.

When at last I reached the Rue Sault-au-Matelot, I found a formidable barricade which served as the center of the lower town's defense. As my men massed for the attack, the city's defenders opened fire from the windows and walls overlooking the street.

During this barrage I was struck in the ankle by a musket ball and had to be carried from the field. Captain Morgan, having assumed command, led the men over this barricade and chased its defenders up the street to a second barricade which he also cleared. He continued on through the town, surmounting numerous additional obstacles as he went. Finally at the gate to Upper Town, Captain Morgan called a halt to wait for General Montgomery. He waited until dawn the following day ar which point he ordered the attack to resume.

This account of the conclusion of the battle was sent by Sir Guy Carleton to General Thomas Gage shortly after Captain Morgan's surrender. You will be surprised to learn that it came to General Washington with several other of the reports I have referred to in this collection of stories from none other

Defending the gate to Upper Town [87]

than General Thomas Gage's wife! Margaret Kemble Gage was a true patriot. It is not commonly known that this heroic woman risked her life to help her country win its freedom. I am sure that she will not mind that you know her secret.

Sir Guy Carleton wrote this:

The Americans reached the gate to the upper city about mid-morning on New Year's Day. There, for some reason, they stopped. During the hours that followed, I brought the garrison into position behind the gate and waited for the next attack. At dawn the following day, the Americans moved forward with ladders to scale the fortress's inner wall. We responded with a heavy fire.

At some point the Americans began to fill the houses on the street before the gate. This allowed them to fire upon us with more deadly effect. The commander of one of my Canadian militias, a man by the name of Charles Charland, led a

Captain Daniel Morgan [88]

detachmnt to the first of these houses. Finding the ladders the invaders had used to enter them, he sent a party of Highlanders and militia up and into the house. After expelling the rebels, our men opened fire on the Americans in the street below. Soon after that, a company of regulars led by Colonel Henry Caldwell came up behind them. Now surrounded, the Americans had no choice but to surrender.

Thus did the battle end for 465 of the attackers. Now only one man stood against us. This was the American leader, a wild frontiersman from Virginia by the name of Daniel Morgan.

Arnold's Flight. Colonel Arnold formed the rearguard for his army's humilitating retreat [89]

Although completely surrounded, Captain Morgan refused to lay down his arms. Instead, he dared us to shoot him, which our gallant men would not do. After much pleading from his comrades, Captain Morgan gave his sword to a French priest rather than surrender it as a gentleman would have done to an officer of his king.

In addition to those who we captured, the rebels lost between sixty and one hundred killed and wounded. Our losses were one naval officer and five Canadian militia killed and four soldiers and fifteen militia wounded. *

---

*Web Source: http://canadachannel.ca/HCO/index. php/2._Battles_of_the_American_Revolution

Colonel Arnold and the remnant of his army continued the siege through the winter. In April, Sir Guy received reinforcements in the form of eleven thousand British regulars and Hessian mercenaries. When they had disembarked from their transports, Sir Guy led a force of 900 men out of the city to attack Colonel Arnold's camp. Colonel Arnold's sick and demoralized troops fled in panic leaving behind most of their artillary, powder and equipment. Fortunately for them, Sir Guy did not care to have more American prisoners since his city was already full.

Colonel Arnold formed the rearguard for his army's humiliating retreat. He kept watch as it crossed the St. Lawrence River to safety. With Sir Guy's troops almost in firing range, he shot his horse and followed them in his canoe.

This marked the end of our misadventure in Canada. It was a low point in our struggle for freedom. You will learn in my next collection of stories that we suffered several more demoralizing defeats in New York, but we overcame them all, because our leaders were determined and the men they led were unselfishly brave. More importantly, our cause was just and God was with us.

Glossary

Reference Source:
The Oxford Universal Dictionary; 3rd Edition. 1955.

Advance Party—A body of troops sent ahead to prepare the way for a column or an army

Artillery—The cannons of war; that branch of an army which manages the cannons of war

Bateau/Bateaux—A Long tapering boat with a flat bottom used by the French Canadians; more than one of these boats

Bedeviled—Tormented or vexed as by a devil

Breastwork—A field work thrown up breast high for defense; a parapet

Cannonade—An assault which is conducted by the continuous discharge of cannon

Column—A formation of troops narrow across and deep from front to rear

Committee of Safety—A body of persons authorized to make and implement policies to promote the safety of the community

Compatriot—A fellow belonging to the same country; one who shares similar feelings and convictions

Condign—Appropriate for or merited by a crime that has been committed

Confiscate—To deprive of property through seizure by the state

Convalescence—The gradual recovery of health after an illness or injury

Dispatch—A written message or communication sent off speedily

Dither—To tremble, quake or vacillate

Embarkation—The act of boarding a ship; undertaking or beginning a new business or enterprise

Glossary

Flagitious—Shameful, wicked, or scandalous

Flank—The extreme right or left side of an army of body of men in military formation

Flotilla—A small fleet; a fleet of small vessels

Fusilier—A soldier in the British army armed with a "fusil" or light musket

Grapeshot—A quantity of small iron balls packed together in a single charge for cannon

Great Carrying Place—In the Highlands of Maine, the wilderness area between the headwaters of the Kennebec River and the Dead River

Grenadier—In the British army, a member of a company of the finest and tallest men in a regiment

Impregnable—Said of a fortress that is capable of resisting all attacks

Indenture/Indentured—A contract which binds an apprentice or servant to a master; to be bound by such a contract

Indissoluble—That which cannot be destroyed or abolished; that which cannot be dissolved or decomposed in a liquid

Lamentable—Full of or expressing sorrow; that which is to be lamented; pitiful or doleful

Loathsome—sickening, odious, repulsive or shocking; that which excites such sentiments

Logistics/Logistical—The art of moving and quartering troops; the art of organizing supplies; that which pertains to these tasks

Machination—The act or process of contriving or planning; a contrivance, intrigue or plot

Martyr—One who suffers death on behalf of any belief of cause; to cause to suffer or to put to death as a martyr

Mercenary—A soldier who is hired to serve in a foreign army

Militia—A military force composed of "citizens" rather than "professional" soldiers

Parade formation—A formation of troops suitable for review but not for battle

Perpetuate/Perpetuator—To continue indefinitely; to preserve from extinction; one who undertakes to do this

Picket—A soldier or small detachment of soldiers sent out to watch for the approach of the enemy; a soldier or small detachment of soldiers held in readiness for service

Porous—To be full of holes through which water, air or light may pass

Practicable—Capable of being carried out or implemented; feasible

Precinct—The space enclosed by the walls of a particular place; an area defined by a line drawn around it

Preconcert/Preconcerted—To arranged beforehand; that which has been arranged beforehand

Provincial—An inhabitant of England's North American colonies prior to the American Revolution

Provisions—A supply of food; a store of necessities of materials

Provocation—An act that incites anger or resentment and invites retaliation

Pyrrhic—Of or pertaining to King Pyrrhus of Epirius in Asia Minor; a victory gained at too great a cost

Repulse—To drive away or beat back by force of arm

Respite—A temporary cessation of labor, war, suffering or the like

Sentry—An armed soldier posted at a specific point to keep guard and prevent the passing of unauthorized persons

Sugar Act—A revenue measure enacted by Parliament in 1764 to draw money from the American colonies for the purpose of funding part of the cost of their ongoing defense

Tory—Originally, someone who opposed the exclusion of James, Duke of York from succession to the Crown of England; later, a member of the political faction that supported policies strengthening the authority of the King over Parliament; prior to and during the American Revolution, colonials who were loyal to the King of England

Treason/ Treacherous—The violation by a subject of his allegiance to his sovereign or his state; said of a person who is disloyal, untrustworthy of false

Trepidation—An instance of confusion or confused alarm

Tyranny/Tyrannical—Oppressive actions or government by an absolute prince; that which is done in an oppressive, cruel or unjust manner

Untenable—That which is indefensible, unsustainable or otherwise unsound

Vindictiveness—An action motivated by a desire for revenge

Volley—A simultaneous discharge of a number of firearms or artillery; a salvo

Picture Credits

The illustrations, portraits, maps and photographs that appear in the text of this book are identified in the following pages. United States copyrights have expired for those that were first published prior to January 1, 1923. These images are therefore in the public domain. Other images are owned by the Library of Congress and other public agencies. These are also in the public domain. Unless otherwise noted, the images that were first published after January 1, 1923 and are not now owned by public agencies are presented under the copyright doctrine of Fair Use which is defined below.

Cover

George Washington and his Troops
Artist: Frank Schoonover (1926)
Owner: Westervelt Company
Tuscaloosa, Alabama
205-562-5000
View online at: http://www.warnermuseum.org/colonialfederal.html

This picture is the property of the Westervelt Collection and displayed in The Westervelt-Warner Museum of American Art in Tuscaloosa, AL. It is used with the owner's permission.

Chapter 1

1   **Alexander Hamilton**

Artist: unknown after a portrait by Charles Willson Peale (c. 1800)
Owner: New York Historical Society Museum
View online at: https://www.nyhistory.org/web/crossroads/gallery/all/
alexander_hamilton_by_unid.html]

Picture Credits

2   **John Murray, 4th Lord Dunmore**
     Artist: Sir Joshua Reynolds (1763)
     Owner: National Galleries of Scotland
     View online at: http://en.wikipedia.org/wiki/File:4thEarlOfDunmore.jpg

3   **Recruiting for the Continental Army**
     Artist: William Tylee Ranney (.c 1850)
     Owner: Unknown
     This image can be purchased at: http://www.1st-art-gallery.com/
     search?q=army&pageno=3

4   **The Culpeper Minute Men Emblem**
     View online at: http://cmmsar.com/

5   **Colonel William Woodford**
     Artist: Unknown
     Owner: Unknown
     View online at: http://darwintern.pbworks.com/w/
     page/16858994/10-2

6   **View at Great Bridge Battle Site**
     Art from: *The pictorial field-book of the revolution or Illustrations, by
     pen and pencil, of the history, biography, scenery, relics, and traditions
     of the war for independence* by Benson John Lossing. Published by
     Harper & Brothers, New York. 1850.
     View online at: http://en.wikipedia.org/wiki/File:Great_Bridge_view_
     Lossing.png

Chapter 2

7   **Washington Takes Command of the Continental Army in Cambridge**
     Engraving by C. Rogers from a painting by M.A. Wageman (c. 1860)
     Owner: The U.S. National Archives and Records Administration
     View online at: http://www.archives.gov/research/military/american-
     revolution/pictures/images/revolutionary-war-016.jpg

8   **The Messenger Came**
     Artist: Mead Shaeffer
     Art from: *Everybody's Washington* by Alden Arthur Knipe. Published
     by Dodd Mead, New York. 1931.
     View online at: http://goldenagecomicbookstories.blogspot.
     com/2009/04/mead-schaeffer-everybodys-washington-by.html

9   **Nathan Hale receiving instructions from Washington**
     Artist: Howard Pyle
     Art from: Harper's Weekly Illustration (1898)
     This image can be purchased at: http://www.1st-art-gallery.com/
     Howard-Pyle/Hale-Receiving-Instructions-From-Washington.html

Picture Credits

10 **Washington Confers with his Generals**
Artist: Howard Pyle
Art from: Harper's Weekly Illustration (c. 1898)
This image can be purchased at: http://www.allposters.com/-sp/Washington-and-His-Generals-in-Consultation-March-15th-1783-Posters_i4144006_.htm

11 **Washington's Farewell to his Officers**
Artist: Alonzo Chappel (c. 1860)
Owner: Unknown
View online at: http://www.alonzochappel.org/Washington's-Farewell-to-his-Officers.html

12 **Lexington Concord Siege of Boston**
Humbly inscribed to Richd. Whitworth by J. De Costa; C. Hall, sc. (1775)
Owner: Library of Congress; American Memory Collection
G3764.B6S3 1775 .D4 Vault, g3764b ar090000
View online at: http://memory.loc.gov/cgi-bin/query/h?ammem/gmd:@field(NUMBER+@band(g3764b+ar090000))

Chapter 3

13 **The Boston Massacre**
Artist: Alonzo Chappel (1868)
Owner: Unknown
View online at: http://www.alonzochappel.org/The-Boston-Massacre,-5th-March-1770.html

14 **The Boston Tea Party**
Art From: Charlotte M. Yonge *Young Folks' History of England* (Boston: D. Lothrop & Co., 1879)
Web Source: http://etc.usf.edu/clipart/29900/29900/bostn_tea_29900.htm

15 **General Thomas Gage**
Artist: John Singleton Copley (1768)
Owner: The Yale Center for British Art
View online at: http://en.wikipedia.org/wiki/File:Thomas_Gage_John_Singleton_Copley.jpeg

16 **Samuel Adams**
Artist: John Singleton Copley (1772)
Owner: Museum of Fine Art, Boston
View online at: http://en.wikipedia.org/wiki/File:J_S_Copley_-_Samuel_Adams.jpg

17 **Paul Revere Observing British Troop Movements**
Web Image

Picture Credits

Chapter 4

Picture Credits

28 **Colonel Benedict Arnold**
Artist: Engraving by H.B. Hall after John Trumbull
Owner: National Archives and Records Administration
View online at: http://publicdomainclip-art.blogspot.com/2010/09/
benedict-arnold.html

29 **British Forts at the time of the American Revolution (French and English names)**
Web Image

30 **Fort Ticonderoga**
Art from: *Quaint and Historic Forts of North America* by John Martin
Hammond. Published by J. B. Lippincott Company, Philadelphia
and London. 1915.
View online at: http://www.accessgenealogy.com/forts/historicforts/
fort_ticonderoga.htm

31 **Ethan Allen Plots the Capture of Ticonderoga at Castleton**
Artist: Harvey Dunn
Art from: Saturday Evening Post Illustration (Fall 1930)
Owner: Dixon Ticonderoga Company
View online at: http://www.dixonusa.com/gallery.cfm

32 **Dawn at Dawn at Ticonderoga, May 10, 1775**
Artist: Harvey Dunn
Art from: Saturday Evening Post Illustration (Fall 1930)
Owner: Dixon Ticonderoga Company
View online at: http://www.dixonusa.com/gallery.cfm

33 **Ethan Allen demands the Surrender of Fort Ticonderoga**
Artist: Alonzo Chappel (c. 1860)
Owner: Unknown
View online at: http://www.historycentral.com/revolt/ticonderoga2.
html

34 **Cannon at Ticonderoga**
Contemporary photograph

35 **Benedict Arnold escaping capture by George Washington's forces on the
Hudson River**
Art from: *A History of the United States for Schools* by Wilbur F. Gordy .
Published by Charles Scribner & Sons, New York. 1916.
View online at: http://etc.usf.edu/clipart/56400/56409/56409_ar-
nold_escap.htm

36 **General Horatio Gates**
Artist: Charles Willson Peale (1782)
Owner: National Park Service – Independence National Historic Park
View online at: http://www.nps.gov/museum/exhibits/revwar/im-
age_gal/indeimg/gates.html#Anchor-Hamilto-17608

36a **General Charles Lee**
    Artist: Gilbert Stuart (c. 1795)
    Owner: Metropolitan Museum of Art, New York
    View online at: http://hoocher.com/Gilbert_Stuart/Gilbert_Stuart.htm

Chapter 5

37 **HMS Active at Anchor in Boston Harbor**
    Artist: Geoff Hunt (N/A)
    Owner: US Department of Commerce, National Oceanic and Atmospheric Administration
    View online at: http://oceanexplorer.noaa.gov/explorations/08auvfest/background/history/media/hms_active.html
    (Note: the Active was the sister ship and of the Cerberus)

38 **General William Howe**
    Artist: Richard Purcell aka Charles Corbutt (1777)
    Owner: Anne S.K. Brown Military History Collection, Brown University
    View online at: http://commons.wikimedia.org/wiki/File:William-howe-fifth-viscount.jpg

39 **General Henry Clinton**
    Artist: Andrea Soldi (c. 1763)
    Owner: The American Museum in Britain
    View online at: http://en.wikipedia.org/wiki/File:Sirhenryclinton2.jpg

40 **General John Burgoyne**
    Artist: Sir Joshua Reynolds (1766)
    Owner: The Frick Museum
    View online at: http://en.wikipedia.org/wiki/File:BurgoyneByReynolds.jpg

41 **A Plan for the Town of Boston**
    Map Maker: Sir Thomas Hyde Page
    Owner: Library of Congress Geography and Map Division Washington, D.C. 20540-4650 USA
    CALL NUMBER: G3764.B6S3 1776 .P3 Faden 33.
    DIGITAL ID: g3764b ct000252 http://hdl.loc.gov/loc.gmd/g3764b.ct000252
    View online at: http://bluemonocle.com/Maps/Product?itemCode=15187

42 **A Plan for the Town of Boston – detail**
    Map Maker: Sir Thomas Hyde Page
    Owner: Library of Congress Geography and Map Division Washington, D.C. 20540-4650 USA
    CALL NUMBER: G3764.B6S3 1776 .P3 Faden 33
    DIGITAL ID: g3764b ct000252 http://hdl.loc.gov/loc.gmd/g3764b.ct000252

Picture Credits

View online at: http://bluemonocle.com/Maps/
Product?itemCode=15187

43 **Colonel William Prescott**
Artist: Frederick Coffay Yohn (c. 1910)
Owner: Unknown
View online at: http://www.superstock.com/
stock-photos-images/900-123066
http://web.mst.edu/~rogersda/umrcourses/ge342/
http//web.mst.edu/~rogersda/umrcourses/ge342/

44 **Bunker Hill**
Artist: John Ward Dunsmore (1937)
Owner: Fraunces Tavern Museum
View online at: http://www.frauncestavernmuseum.org

45 **Bunker Hill**
Artist: Howard Pyle (1897)
Owner: Delaware Art Museum
View online at: http://www.theamericanrevolution.org/battledetail.
aspx?battle=5

46 **The Death of General Warren**
Artist: John Trumbull (1786)
Owner: Museum of Fine Arts, Boston
View online at: http://en.wikipedia.org/wiki/File:The_death_of_gen-
eral_warren_at_the_battle_of_bunker_hill.jpg

47 **Major General Israel Putnam at the Battle of Bunker Hill (far left)**
*Detail from - The Death of General Warren at the Battle of Bunker's
Hill, June 17,1775.*
Artist: John Trumbull (1786)
Owner: Museum of Fine Arts, Boston
View online at: http://en.wikipedia.org/wiki/File:The_death_of_gen-
eral_warren_at_the_battle_of_bunker_hill.jpg

Chapter 6

48 **George Washington taking command of the Army, 1775**
Art from: The Life and Times of Washington, Volume I.
Artist: Alonzo Chappel (1857)
View online at: http://www.alonzochappel.org/George-Washington-
taking-command-of-the-Army,-1775,-from-'Life-and-Times-of-
Washington',-Volume-I,--1857-large.html

49 **Continental Army Recruits Training**
Web image
View online at: http://cpwv.org/wp-content/uploads/2010/06/6-
14-1776-Continental-Army.jpg

Picture Credits

Chapter 7

Picture Credits

61 **Brigadier General Richard Montgomery**
Artist: G. R. Hall after a painting by Alonzo Chappel (1909)
Owner: Unknown
View online at: http://www.iment.com/maida/familytree/henry/bios/
richardmontgomery.htm

62 **Colonel Benedict Arnold**
Artist: Thomas Hart (March 26, 1776)
Owner: Anne S. K. Brown Collection at Brown University
http://en.wikipedia.org/wiki/File:Benedict_Arnold_1color.jpg
View online at: http://www.iment.com/maida/familytree/henry/bios/
richardmontgomery.htm

63 **The American Attack on Quebec in 1775**
Map by: United States Army Center of Military History, vector ver-
sion by Fvasconcellos (1989)
View online at: http://en.wikipedia.org/wiki/File:American_at-
tack_on_Quebec.svg

64 **Fort Crown Point – Model**
Contemporary Photograph
View online at: http://flintlockandtomahawk.blogspot.
com/2009_08_30_archive.html

65 **The Embarkation of Montgomery's troops at Crown Point (1902)**
Artist: Unknown
Library of Congress Prints and Photographs Division
Reproduction Number LC-USZ62-108230
View online at: http://www.americaslibrary.gov/jb/revolut/jb_revo-
lut_canada_1_e.html

66 **Champlain Valley (1777)**
Owner: Norman B. Leventhal Map Center at the Boston Public Library
Call Number: G3711.S3 1777 .B75 URL
View online at: http://maps.bpl.org/details_10101/

67 **Fort-Saint-Jean**
Artist: pen and ink painting by James Peachey (c. 1775)
Owner: National Archives of Canada
View online at: http://everitas.rmcclub.ca/?p=29340

68 **Firing on Fort St Jean**
Web image

69 **Montreal**
Artist: pen and ink painting by James Peachey (c. 1775)
Owner: National Archives of Canada
*View online at: http://www.canadachannel.ca/HCO/index.php/
File:M1MONTREAL.JPG*

Picture Credits

70   **The Isles of Montreal**
      Map by the French engineers (1761)
      Owner: Boston Public Library, Norman B. Leventhal Map Center
      View online at: http://maps.bpl.org/details_14104/?srch_
         query=Montreal&srch_fields=all&srch_style=exact&srch_fa=save

71   **The Surrender of Montreal (1760)**
      Web Image
      View online at: http://www.uppercanadahistory.ca/wm/wm8.html

72   **Fortress Quebec**
      Web Image
      View online at: http://richardnelson.org/Parent-Frost%20Website/A%20
         SHORT%20HISTORY%20OF%20NEW%20FRANCE.htm

73   **A View of the Citadel of Quebec**
      Web Image
      View online at: http://www.sonofthesouth.net/revolutionary-war/
         colonies/quebec.htm

74   **Quebec City Walls**
      Contemporary Photograph

Chapter 8

75   **The Bateaux on the Dead River**
      Artist: NC Wyeth (1931)
      Owner: Unknown
      View online at: http://benningswritingpad.blogspot.
         com/2006_02_01_archive.html

76   **Map published by Henry Delahoy Symonds of New England in 1795**
      Owner: The Boston Public Library Map Collection
      View online at: http://en.wikipedia.org/wiki/File:ArnoldExpeditionR
         outeMarked.jpg

77   **Aaron Burr**
      Artist: Attributed to Gilbert Stuart (1792)
      Library of Congress
      http://portrevolt.com/images/gallery/v/gilbert_stuart/aaron_burr.html

78   **The Kennebec and Chaudiere River Route to Quebec**
      Map by: Robert R. Baldwin (1776)
      Owner: Boston Public Library, Morton B. Leventhal Map Center
      Call Number: G3732.K4S3 1776 .V5
      View online at: http://maps.bpl.org/details_10874/?mtid=103

79   **Joliet and Marquette traversed a portage between the Great Lakes and the
      Mississippi River System with the help of Indian guides (1673)**
      Owner: Library of Congress

Picture Credits

View online at: http://adventure.howstuffworks.com/chicago-por-tage-national-historic-site.htm

80 **Working against the flood on Dead River (c. 1903)**
Library of Congress, Prints and Photographs Division
Reproduction Number LC-USZ62-108233.
View online at: http://www.americaslibrary.gov/jb/revolut/jb_revo-lut_canada_2_e.html

81 **Whitewater on the Chaudiere River**
Webb Image
View online at: http://www.kellscraft.com/MainePioneer/MainePio-neerCh22.html

82 **Several boats were lost descending the Chaudiere River**
Webb Image

83 **Sir Guy Carleton reviewing his troops in Quebec**
Web Image

84 **The Death of General Montgomery**
Artist: Alonzo Chappel (1865)
Owner: Unknown
View online at: http://www.alonzochappel.org/Death-of-General-Richard-Montgomery-on-31st-December-1775,-1865.html

85 **Canadian militiamen and British soldiers repulse the American assault at Sault-au-Matelot**
Artist: Allen Daniel
Cover art for: *The father of British Canada: a chronicle of Carleton, Volume 12* by William Wood. Toronto. 1916.
View online at: http://upload.wikimedia.org/wikipedia/commons/e/eb/Canadian_militiamen_and_British_soldiers_repulse_the_Amer-ican_assault_at_Sault-au-Matelot.jpg
http://www.citizendia.org/Battle_of_Quebec_(1775)
Photograph Courtesy of the Canadian Department of Defense

86 **Margaret Kemble Gage**
Artist: John Singleton Copley (1771)
Timkin Gallery of Art, San Diego CA
View online at: http://en.wikipedia.org/wiki/File:Margaret_Kemble_Gage.jpg

87 **Defending the Gate to Upper town**
Artist: Engraving by F. H. Wellington based on painting by Sidney Adamson (date unknown)
Owner: Library and Archives of Canada – C005415
View online at: http://www.mcq.org/place-royale/en/themes.php?id=9&ver=1

Picture Credits

88 **Captain Daniel Morgan**
Artist: Charles Willson Peale (1794)
Owner: Independence National Historical Park
View online at: http://en.wikipedia.org/wiki/File:DanielMorgan.jpeg

89 **Arnold's Flight**
Web Image
View online at: http://ushistoryimages.com/benedict-arnold.shtm

Fair Use:

"Fair use" refers to a doctrine found in United States copyright law under which limited use of copyrighted material may be made without requiring permission from the rights holder. Section 107 of the copyright law (title 17, U.S. Code) contains a list of the various purposes for which the reproduction of a particular work may be considered fair, such as criticism, comment, news reporting, teaching, scholarship, and research. It also sets out four factors to be considered in determining whether or not a particular use is fair:

1. The purpose and character of the use, including whether such use is of commercial nature or is for nonprofit educational purposes
2. The nature of the copyrighted work
3. The amount and substantiality of the portion used in relation to the copyrighted work as a whole
4. The effect of the use upon the potential market for, or value of, the copyrighted work

The use of particular images in this text is deemed to be covered by the fair use doctrine on these grounds:

1. Because none of the images in this book are of commercial quality or size, or reproduced in color, they are only suggestive of the original works.
2. The images that appear in the text of the book are of minor significance to the ideas its stories convey.
3. No image in this book is necessary to complete a story contained in the text.
4. The presentation of the images that appear in the text has no material impact on the value of the works of art that they depict.
5. The intent of the book is to educate its readers.

About the Author

JAMES M. BAYNE holds degrees from Univ. of Illinois and Harvard Business School. He is a veteran of the US Army, the Illinois Militia and the Illinois National Guard. During his four-decade business career, he was an architect and structural engineer with Smith, Hinchman and Grylls, Inc. in Detroit; a partner in Bayne and Lee, Architects and then became a member of NASA's original Space Task Group where he served as Director of Design for the Manned (now Johnson) Space Center in Houston; he then became Director of Engineering for the Electronics Research Center, Cambridge, MA and concluded his government service at NASA Headquarters in Washington, DC.

In addition to memberships in numerous professional organizations and societies, Mr. Bayne is a Mason, Knight Templar and an American Legionnaire. He also holds membership in the Jamestowne Society, First Families of America, the Order of Founders and Patriots of America, the Culpeper Minute Men Chapter of the Sons of the American Revolution (which he served as President), the Virginia Society of the Sons of the American Revolution (which he served as President), the War of 1812 Society and the Scottish-American Military Society. He is a Chevalier in the Sovereign Military Order of the Temple of Jerusalem, a Fellow in the Antiquaries

Society of Scotland, and has served as 2nd Deputy Governor of the Virginia Chapter of the Sons and Daughters of the Pilgrims.

Mr. Bayne was inspired to write a column remembering America's patriotic heritage after reading an article in his local paper celebrating Cinco de Mayo. These vignettes he wrote in the course of this three year enterprise are the source material for Commonwealth Books' "Stories for Young Readers" series.

CPSIA information can be obtained at www.ICGtesting.com

260671BV00006B/1/P

9 780982 592243